DATE DUE

CO ONS

About the Author

George Thorman is a former member of the faculty of
the graduate School of Social Work at the University of
Texas and St. Edward's University in Austin. A clinical
social worker, Mr. Thorman has engaged in a wide range
of casework practice and conducted workshops throughout Texas for several years. He has written articles for
professional journals and is the author of several books
including *Family Violence, Incestuous Families, Day Care:
An Emerging Crisis, Homeless Families* and *Emotional Problems of Aging.*

COUNSELING OLDER PERSONS
A Professional Handbook

By

GEORGE THORMAN, M.A., M.S.W.

CHARLES C THOMAS • PUBLISHER
Springfield • Illinois • U.S.A.

Published and Distributed Throughout the World by

CHARLES C THOMAS • PUBLISHER
2600 South First Street
Springfield, Illinois 62794-9265

© *1995 by* CHARLES C THOMAS • PUBLISHER

ISBN 0-398-05993-4   (cloth)
ISBN 0-398-05994-2   (paper)

Library of Congress Catalog Card Number: 95-2561

With **THOMAS BOOKS** *careful attention is given to all details of manufacturing
and design. It is the Publisher's desire to present books that are satisfactory as to their
physical qualities and artistic possibilities and appropriate for their particular use.*
THOMAS BOOKS *will be true to those laws of quality that assure a good name
and good will.*

Printed in the United States of America
SC-R-3

Library of Congress Cataloging-in-Publication Data

Thorman, George.
   Counseling older persons : a professional handbook / George
Thorman.
      p.   cm.
   Includes bibliographical references and index.
   ISBN 0-398-05993-4 (cloth). — ISBN 0-398-05994-2 (pbk.)
   1. Psychotherapy for the aged.   2. Aged—Counseling of.
I. Title.
RC480.54.T48   1995
618.97′68914—dc20   95-2561
                                                         CIP

CONTENTS

		Page
Introduction		3
Section I	Objectives of Geriatric Counseling	5
Section II	The Counseling Process	9
Section III	Approaches to Counseling	15
Section IV	Psychosocial Therapy	23
Section V	Problem Solving	29
Section VI	Integrative Counseling	37
Section VII	Behavioral and Cognitive Therapy	43
Section VIII	Crisis Intervention	53
Section IX	Adjuncts to Counseling	61
Section X	Group Therapy	73
Section XI	Coping with Dying	83
Selected References		91
Appendix		93
Index		103

COUNSELING OLDER PERSONS
A Professional Handbook

INTRODUCTION

A growing interest in gerontology and new attitudes toward aging have led to a better understanding of the needs of older persons and the development of new approaches to helping them cope with serious physical, mental and emotional problems. The high rate of suicide among the elderly and the incidence of mental illness in later life indicate that serious attention must be given to the critical problems of aging. Counseling older persons has now become recognized as an effective way to minimize the negative impact of aging and help elderly persons achieve and maintain higher quality of life.

Although the majority of older persons are able to cope with aging, a significant number need help in one or more critical areas of functioning. Therefore, geriatric counseling is not the exclusive domain of any one professional group. It includes physicians, nutritionists and nurses who can provide medical and physical care and social workers who can provide psychological support and a safe environment for older persons. Psychologists who are skilled in the use of behavior modification and cognitive therapy can help aged persons change behavior patterns, gain self-confidence and improve their problem-solving capacity. Institutional settings can provide special forms of group therapy that improve social and cognitive functioning. Counselors who are skilled in family therapy, marriage counseling and sex therapy can provide help in resolving family problems, marital conflict and sexual difficulties.

I have prepared this handbook to serve as a guide for counselors and mental health workers who undertake the important task of helping older persons cope with the problems that accompany aging. We have neglected our elderly too long; we must no longer fail to provide the services they need and richly deserve.

I. OBJECTIVES OF GERIATRIC COUNSELING

Geriatric counseling is concerned with the physical, mental, emotional and social well-being of elderly persons. To accomplish this overall objective, counseling is directed toward certain specific goals: increasing client's self-esteem; improving their problem-solving skills; helping them cope with loss, resolve crisis situations, and deal with stress.

Increasing Self-Esteem. The aging process often diminishes self-esteem and produces feelings of inadequacy or worthlessness as individuals grow old. Basic physical changes can be a traumatic experience. Changes in appearance, wrinkling of the skin, baldness and graying hair affect how persons see themselves. Women are especially vulnerable to such changes and think of themselves as unattractive. As they age, men lose muscular strength and become concerned about their endurance or their ability to perform strenuous physical tasks.

Changes in mental alertness and cognitive functioning also leave a significant negative impact on self-esteem. Difficulty in remembering, so often associated with aging, causes older persons to question their ability to reason. A slowdown in these mental functions is especially traumatic for those who take pride in their ability to carry out tasks that require logical, coherent thought.

Commonly accepted stereotypes about aging also damage self-esteem. Myths that aged persons are senile, unproductive and disengaged from the world around them can cause the elderly to view themselves as worthless. Overly protective responses from friends and relatives reinforce these feelings of inadequacy and helplessness. Psychological support and ego-building strategies can help clients overcome these attitudes and enable them to fulfill their potential in later life.

Increasing Problem-Solving Ability. Older persons differ in their ability to deal with problem situations. Those who have serious difficulty coping with problems become anxious or depressed. Geriatric counseling helps clients learn to solve various problems. As they begin to rely on their own resources and skills, their sense of adequacy and self-worth increases. Training in problem solving is especially beneficial when older persons are going through a transition that involves change in roles or status. Women who become widows and face important decisions can benefit from problem-solving counseling. As they develop ability to cope with everyday life situations, they become more confident and less anxious.

Coping With Loss. Aging often brings about severe losses that create anxiety and depression. As persons age, they are likely to experience the death of an important person in their lives. Older women usually survive the death of the husband and are called upon to cope with the loneliness that comes with the end of an important relationship. The emotional impact of such a loss can be eased by counseling. Supportive measures help survivors cope with the loneliness and grief that come with the death of a loved one. All persons need a confidant with whom they can share their feelings. In many instances, a professional counselor may fill this role and ease the distress that follows an important loss. The catharsis of grieving lays the groundwork for a renewed sense of self and the beginning of new attachments that will give meaning and purpose to life.

One of the most complex forms of counseling is required when individuals are terminally ill and are called upon to face the reality of their own death. Helping people die with dignity requires great sensitivity. To work with the dying, counselors need to be aware of their own feeling about death and accept dying as a natural part of life. Providing safe conduct from life to death is a difficult and frustrating task, but it is one that can also be rewarding and satisfying.

Resolving Crisis Situations. Older persons may face other types of situations that present a crisis of major significance. Changes in status or loss of important social roles may threaten to disturb the emotional balance of older persons because they are especially sensitive to an interruption of established life patterns. Counseling helps them cope with the trauma associated with these events. Through prompt intervention, mental health workers enable older persons to mobilize internal and external resources, make decisions and embark on a course of action that will resolve the crisis. Counseling tries to restore the client to a pre-crisis leveling of functioning within a relatively short period of time and avoid serious long-term serious problems. Although crisis intervention focuses on the immediate problem to be resolved, it can also lead to the development of more adequate mechanisms for coping with future problems.

In some cases, older clients also need to be involved in a long-term supportive relationship after the crisis has been resolved and the counseling process may continue in order to insure that clients are able to function adequately without the help of the worker.

Reducing Stress. Older persons are likely to undergo severe stress at a time when they are not adequately equipped to deal with new situations. Counseling can significantly reduce anxiety and feelings of helplessness that are associated with stressful situations. As clients gain confidence in their ability to cope with stress, their anxiety is significantly reduced because they feel that they are in control of their lives.

Environmental factors that have a negative impact on older persons are sources of stress. Persons who live in an unsafe, crime-ridden community often present ideation that has a strong paranoid orientation. Although these symptoms may suggest abnormal anxiety and suspicion, there is usually some basis for such reactions. Being the victim of a mugger must be recognized as a real possibility for older persons who are often the targets of street crime. Measures that are designed to protect older persons are needed to reduce the level of stress for those who live in an unsafe social environment.

Lack of financial resources is also a significant source of stress for many older persons, especially those who are completely dependent on the limited income provided by Social Security. The high cost of medications is a constant concern for those who are suffering from chronic illnesses that require expensive pharmaceuticals and leave older persons without enough money to pay for decent housing and good nutrition.

A social policy that gives high priority to the financial needs of an older person is essential if these external stresses are to be reduced or eliminated. The problem of stress management must be seen in a different perspective. As one mental health expert points out, the traditional medical approach to the treatment of mental disorders often fails to take into account factors outside the person as sources of emotional and mental disorders in older persons:

> Because of the tendency to view old persons as impaired due to their age, excessive use of the medical model and its variants reinforces the likelihood that one will blame a problem on something inside the person and miss those factors in the individual's environment that are influencing or controlling the disturbed behavior (Zarit, p. 117).

Geriatric counselors can play an important role in promoting the development of social programs that will enhance the lives of older Americans, including low-cost housing, adequate health care and financial assistance.

II. THE COUNSELING PROCESS

The counseling process involves five different but interrelated procedures: (1) establishing a working relationship with the client; (2) exploring the client's problems; (3) assessing the problems; (4) setting goals; (5) planning intervention strategies.

Establishing a Working Relationship. Older persons have conflicting feelings about accepting help. They tend to view counseling as a sign of weakness—a perception that prevents them from seeking the help they need. Counselors who are sensitive to the resistance of older persons can take measures that lead to a close working relationship with their clients.

Corey has suggested that effective counseling depends in large measure on the personal qualities of those who are working with the elderly. Among these qualities are the following:

1. genuine respect for old people
2. positive experience with old people
3. a deep sense of caring for the elderly
4. ability and desire to learn from older persons
5. understanding the biological aspects of aging
6. knowledge of the psychological needs of the aged
7. a conviction that later life can be challenging
8. sensitivity to the burdens and anxieties of the aged
9. ability to challenge myths about aging
10. a healthy attitude regarding one's own eventual old age.

Studies indicate that elderly persons are keenly sensitive to the perceptions and attitudes of others. They know when they are accepted and know when they are rejected or merely tolerated. It is essential that geriatric counselors show a genuine respect for older persons at the very beginning of their work with aged clients. Failure to accord genuine acceptance and respect has important consequences.

Robert Butler, has coined the term **ageism** which he describes as "a process of systematic stereotyping and discrimination against people because they are old, just as racism and sexism accomplish this with skin color and gender" (Butler, 12). Butler suggests that psychiatrists and mental health workers can be caught up in ageism and may fail to provide the high quality of care the elderly deserve.

This attitude toward the elderly has been shown to be a barrier that older clients often face in obtaining help. A widespread and accepted pessimism about the outcome of therapy with the aged is based on the belief that they are inflexible and cannot benefit from counseling. Therefore, the mental health of the elderly has not been given a high priority by the helping professions. However, gerontologists are now beginning to challenge the view that problems of aging are entirely biological and therefore inevitable and irreversible. Progress in accepting older persons as individuals who deserve careful attention to their problems holds promise for the future.

Exploring Problems. Establishing a positive relationship between counselor and client leads to an exploration of their problems. Some older persons will present more than one problem. Some will have difficulty giving a clear and concise statement that accurately defines their problem. Considerable patience is required at this stage of counseling so clients can talk about their situation in a leisurely and informal way. Among the questions that need to be answered are these:

1. How does the client perceive the problem? What is the general area of concern: health? finances? loss of important others? inability to function normally?
2. How does the client describe the origin of the problem? A history will reveal whether the problem has been longstanding, has a recent origin or is related to a specific event.
3. Has the client faced a given problem previously? How did he/she attempt to cope with it?
4. What does the client think might resolve the problem? Does he/she take a pessimistic or optimistic view about the possibility of dealing with the current situation?
5. How does the client expect counseling to be useful in solving the presented problem? Does the client expect to receive advice? Concrete services? Health Care? Financial assistance?
6. Does the client want to change? What are his/her goals for the future? Do these goals seem to be attainable?
7. Does the client reveal any problems about his/her emotional

state?: "nervous tension," "nervous stomach," "worry all the time?" Suicidal thought? Excessive use of drugs and alcohol?

Answers to these questions will provide information on which a more formal assessment can be based. In addition, clues to the client's problems often come from direct observation by the counselor. Among these are the following:

1. Manifestation of difficulty in walking, speaking, eyesight or hearing.
2. Indications that the client has memory loss, is mentally disturbed or suffers from confusion in thinking.
3. Symptoms of emotional disturbance: depression, anxiety, or phobic fears.

These and other observations are taken into account in determining whether physical or psychological impairments are involved and if they create a major problem for the client.

Setting Goals. The assessment process leads to the formulation of a plan of action that is seen as an effective solution to the client's problems. This plan involves a determination of the goals that are perceived as essential to a successful outcome.

Setting goals requires collaboration between client and counselor. Therefore, goals are stated in terms that the client understands. After the goals have been clarified, the client may want to modify or reject one or more of them because they are perceived to have little or no relevance to his/her problem. Once clients indicate which goals are acceptable, priorities may be established in order of their importance.

Planning Intervention

Counselors are called upon to fill several roles in working with the elderly: enabler, teacher, social broker, and mediator. Each of these roles plays an important part in helping older persons cope with problems.

Clients need to understand what role the counselor will play in the helping process. Elderly persons enter into counseling with confused expectations. Unless these expectations are explored and the role of the counselor is clearly defined, older clients are inclined to drop out of counseling because they see the counselor as ineffective. Therefore, a successful outcome requires the counselor to explain what role he/she will play in the helping process.

Enabler. As enablers, counselors direct their efforts toward assisting clients to find coping strengths within themselves to achieve desired changes. By offering reassurance and psychological support, the counselor acts as a facilitator when clients express low esteem and lack confidence in their mental and emotional capacity to resolve problems and cope with crisis.

Teacher. The teaching role is basic in all models of counseling. In the course of working with the elderly they learn how to approach problem situations in a rational, orderly way. They also learn how to control anxiety and understand the sources of their depression. The role of teacher is often more acceptable to older persons because they may not feel that they need therapy for some personal inadequacy or deviant behavior. Rather, they perceive themselves as students looking to the counselor who has special expertise and from whom they can learn and who can provide them with the information they need for decision making.

Mediator. Some older persons are experiencing difficulties in relationship to their adult children or other persons who play an important role in their lives. Differences among family members may result in rifts and splits that are damaging to an older client. In such cases, the counselor assists the client to find a common ground on which the conflict can be resolved. Through persuasion and conciliation, the counselor helps each party identify their common interest in bringing about a successful outcome and avoiding prolonged and devastating conflict.

Social Broker. Many elderly persons are faced with multiple problems that require the services of several helping agencies. The primary role of the counselor as social broker is to steer people to the existing services that can benefit them and help older persons negotiate the complex pathway to obtain them. The counselor needs to possess a working knowledge of available services and match them to meet the older client's particular needs. Serving as a social broker also requires a knowledge of the operating procedures of community agencies so that clients will take the steps that make them eligible to receive help.

Any of these roles can be used to achieve a successful outcome in counseling the elderly, and they may be used in conjunction with one another.

Evaluation

Clients and counselors should be involved in a continuous process of evaluating the effectiveness of the helping process. Evaluating is a mutual undertaking in which clients give the counselor feedback about their experiences in trying to bring about improvement in their personal functioning and their life situation. This mutual evaluation process gives clients an opportunity to express their views as to whether any progress has been made to achieve certain specified goals. Both client and counselor must have a clear understanding and agreement about goals in order that an evaluation can be made. Clients also need to have a clear understanding of the specific nature of the intervention plan and procedure to determine if the helping process does or does not lead to the accomplishment of certain goals. Evaluation counseling may present some difficulty because the results cannot be accurately measured. A goal-attainment scale has been developed by Kiersuh and Garwick to measure progress in mental health programs. (See Appendix). This scale is useful because it permits goals to be suited to each individual client. The behavior modification approach can measure progress in terms of the frequency with which specific behavior occurs. The task-centered approach lends itself to a similar evaluation by determining if assigned tasks have been completed and if they have been effective in solving the client's problem.

The procedure for evaluating the progress of older persons who are diagnosed as suffering from an emotional disorder depends on the client's self-reports and clinical observation. A client who has a mood disorder such as depression may experience relief from some of the distressing symptoms of the illness. For example, the client may report a noticeable diminution of deep feelings of sadness and insomnia. Complaints of diminished ability to think or concentrate may be absent, and suicide ideation may no longer be in evidence. As more of the symptoms are eliminated, the evaluation indicates steady progress to mental health and restoration of functioning.

Formal periodic evaluations can be the basis for making important decisions about the course counseling pursues. Supplementary measures can be put in place to reinforce the client's progress. For example, depressed patients may be referred to a special retirement counseling program if their emotional discomfort is related to a change in their emotional status when they are no longer in the work force. In some cases, several approaches may be combined to further client's progress.

Termination

There is considerable variation as to what criteria determine whether counseling should be terminated. However, most practitioners agree that a planned termination is favored over an unplanned discontinuance and should be based on a mutual agreement between the client and the counselor.

Several problems may prevent a planned termination. Among these are the following:

1. The client may cling to the counselor after the presented problem has been resolved.
2. Problems may suddenly emerge again and in aggravated form.
3. Entirely new problems may be presented in the last interview.
4. The practitioner may delay termination to support a client's wish to continue in counseling.

If difficulties arise, it is important for the counselor to help clients deal with their discomfort about termination and the loss of a counselor who has become a very important source of help. Counseling involves a certain degree of dependence that many clients experience. Counselors may be a vital source of advice and affection for older persons who feel isolated and neglected. However, counselors should make sure that clients are fully informed about other resources that are available and are assured that they can keep in touch with the counselor. If they really need help with another problem, they may return for additional help.

III. APPROACHES TO COUNSELING

Among the most frequently used forms of counseling are: psychosocial therapy, supportive casework, task-centered practice, crisis intervention, behavior modification, cognitive therapy and integrative counseling. Although these models share the common objective of enabling older persons to achieve and maintain a high quality of lie, each approach has a different emphasis and a unique structure.

Psychosocial Therapy. This approach emphasizes the way in which the counselor can enhance and restore the well-being of older persons and help them function more adequately in their social relationships. Psychosocial therapy is designed to promote personal growth, reduce current life pressures and strengthen the ego functioning of clients as they approach old age. Through counseling, clients are engaged in examining distortions in their perception of reality and the way in which they use defense mechanisms when confronted with problems. The counselor helps the client acquire insight into the ways in which intra-psychic conflicts interfere in their relationship to others and inhibits the ability to cope with problems constructively.

Although psychosocial therapy tends to emphasize psychodynamic factors as the underlying cause of dysfunctioning, counselors who use this approach also consider the social environment to be an important factor in the life of the elderly. Psychosocial therapy includes efforts to eliminate or reduce external sources of stress that impair social functioning and prevent elderly clients from achieving their full potential.

Crisis Intervention. Crisis intervention is a method whereby a client is helped to cope with a crisis situation and a loss of emotional balance due to stress. Crisis intervention is a short-term form of counseling and focuses on the present problem and the event or events that brought on a crisis. There is some disagreement about time limits, but practitioners agree that help should be offered as soon as possible after the onset of the problem. Although this approach focuses on the client's immediate problem, this model can be used to help elderly persons develop mechanisms for coping with future problems.

Crisis intervention is used in working with a wide range of human problems. Some crises are situational, such as illness, death, retirement, and other abrupt changes that threaten survival and produce much anxiety about the future. Some crises are developmental in nature and occur when older people move from a life stage in which they are competent and independent to a point where they are less capable and mostly rely on others.

Crisis intervention is especially useful in working with the elderly because they are likely to experience personal losses that bring about significant changes in their life situation. Loss of health and loss of social status may produce a high level of anxiety and emotional trauma. In such cases, prompt intervention can help elderly clients regain a sense of emotional balance and restore them to a pre-crisis level of functioning.

Task-Centered Counseling. Task-centered practice is a systematic way to alleviate particular problems that clients acknowledge and with which they want help because they are in a state of distress. Attention is focused on a **target** problem, i.e., the problem that the client and counselor regard as the primary concern. After the target problem has been clearly stated, the client and counselor determine what tasks need to be undertaken if the problem is to be resolved. Tasks are broken down into specific steps or acts that clients agree to complete.

This model can be used in dealing with a variety of personal, interpersonal and situational problems. It is particularly appropriate in working with older clients because they are more comfortable when they have a clear understanding of what needs to be done. Older persons respond to a structured approach to problem solving and a framework that is aimed at alleviating a well-defined problem. Unlike psychodynamic models of counseling, the task-centered approach does not involve lengthy diagnostic appraisal. Rather than give attention to the psychodynamics of the client's feeling or behavior, this model is highly pragmatic in approach and focuses on developing actions that clients can take to solve a given problem.

Behavior Modification. Behavior modification can be briefly defined as an attempt to decrease maladaptive behavior and increase adaptive behavior. Therapy consists of training clients to respond to specific situations in new ways and increase their behavioral repertoire. When applied to older persons, it can help them control anxiety and resolve emotional disorders.

Behavior modification is based on social learning theory and stands in contrast to traditional psychotherapy that regards abnormal behavior as symptomatic of a basic personality disturbance or underlying conflict. The behavioral approach is based on the premise that emotional problems represent maladaptive behavior that the individual has learned and that behavior can be changed through the use of specific techniques such as systematic desensitation to situations that provoke anxiety or depression.

For older persons, the techniques of behavior modification can be employed to help them cope with specific fears such as fear of being alone, fear of rejection, fear of being institutionalized because of a physical or mental disorder. Training in progressive relaxation is helpful in teaching clients how to reduce tension in stress-producing situations. Combined with mental imagery in which clients are instructed to imagine situations that create anxiety, this exercise enables older persons to cope with emotional reactions that interfere with normal functioning.

Cognitive Therapy. Cognitive therapy is designed to eliminate psychological distress by correcting faulty perceptions and irrational thought patterns that underlie anxiety, depression and other emotional or behavioral disorders. Cognitive therapy is based on the premise that an individual's problems are derived from certain distortions of reality based on erroneous assumptions. Therapy is aimed at helping clients unravel these distortions in thinking and learn more realistic ways of formulating their experiences.

The most well-known form of cognitive therapy is "rational-emotive therapy" developed by Albert Ellis. According to Ellis, emotional problems, such as depression are not caused by outside events but how these events which are interpreted and evaluated. Therefore, helping people cope with emotional problems involves questioning, challenging and disputing the irrational belief that causes them to become depressed, fearful or hopeless. The purpose of this process is to enable people to recognize that their beliefs are absurd, relinquish them and adopt new ways of responding to emotionally disturbing situations and events.

Many emotional problems, especially depression, appear to be related to certain patterns of thinking among the elderly. Older persons frequently think of themselves as inadequate and incompetent. Cognitive therapy is designed to question this perception and replace it with a positive pattern of thought that results in greater self-esteem and a sense of masterful control that reduces depression and anxiety. In view of the fact that older persons experience many losses, this approach can be useful in helping them respond to these traumatic experiences in new ways and reduce their impact on mental and emotional functioning.

Integrative Counseling. The integrative approach to helping the elderly is an outgrowth of the work of Edmund Sherman who suggested that an eclectic method of counseling is best suited to solve the problems of aging. The underlying theme of the integrative method is expressed by Sherman. "The central focus of the approach is to identify, use and enhance the normal development of personality functioning in the later years of adulthood as the basis for counseling older persons" (p. 27).

The integrative approach is not based on any one theoretical frame of reference. Indeed, the term **integrative** suggests that the model borrows useful knowledge and concepts from several sources and attempts to integrate the views of various schools of psychotherapy into a comprehensive form of intervention. However, it is unique in that the model focuses on the importance of the values and morale as prime issues in working with the elderly. Integrative counseling is concerned with the quality of life of older persons and helps them avoid feelings of uselessness and hopelessness that results in despair. Sherman suggests that in an important sense, "the integrative approach is psychophilosophy, and the key to the whole approach is compassionate acceptance of self—past present and future."

The major models of counseling have some similarities and some distinguishable differences in theoretical orientation and techniques. All of them provide a framework for problem solving and assists older persons in developing skills that can be transferred to a wide range of situations. No one approach is the only way of helping. Indeed, a combination of various models may be the most effective approach in many situations.

Core Conditions of Counseling

Every approach to counseling has highlighted the significance of relationship between client and counselors. Yet the term "relationship" is difficult to define. Most definitions tend to take on a rather mystical nature and make only vague references to the specific interaction between therapist and client that is essential to a successful outcome of the helping process. Rapoport summarizes the problem in the following succinct way: "Relationship is a rather fuzzy concept since we cannot state with clarity what aspect of relationship, what kind, what symbolic value, what degree of intensity are essential ingredients of treatment."

In an effort to clarify the meaning of relationship in therapy, Carl Rogers identified three components that are essential in the helping process: **empathy, warmth** and **genuineness**. These dimensions are generally regarded as useful in analyzing what is the nature of the helping relationship.

Accurate empathy refers to the ability of the therapist to perceive and communicate the feelings and experience of another person. Being empathetic means more than simply understanding another person's world. It means **communicating** that understanding through a continuous sharing of what the client is attempting to communicate. Such active interaction ensures that errors in the counselor's perception can be quickly recognized and modified. Accurate empathy also means more than simple understanding. The focus is on feelings, particularly the client's current feelings. Not only is the therapist sensitive to exposed feelings, but is intent on helping the client explore underlying emotions that the client is trying to communicate but somehow cannot express. At a higher level of empathy, the therapist not only communicates an understanding of the client's superficial feelings, but also communicates an understanding of the client's deeper feelings by tone of voice, actual words and facial expression.

Non-possessive warmth refers to the therapist's communication of respect, liking and concern for the client in a non-demanding or dominating manner. Non-possessive warmth means that the therapist accepts the client as a person with human potentials. The behavior and thoughts of the client are not evaluated in judgmental terms. The therapist does not need to sanction or approve the client's behavior, but does accept the client despite such thoughts or behavior.

Therapists may express warmth in various degrees of intensity. Truax and Corkhuff (p. 60–67) describe the highest level of non-possessive warmth as follows:

> There is a deep respect for the patient's worth as a person and his rights as a free individual. At this level the patient is free to be himself even if this means that he is regressing, being defensive, or even disliking or rejecting the therapist himself.

At the lowest level of warmth, the therapist gives responses that tell the client that his/her behavior is being evaluated. If the therapist refrains from such negative responses, the client feels free to express feelings that might otherwise remain unexpressed.

The term "acceptance" has been used to describe the way in which the therapist relates to the client. Acceptance, however, involves more than a passive stance. It is based on a positive belief that every person has a capacity to grow and mature, and each individual is striving in his or her own way to cope with problems and survive despite difficulties and serious obstacles.

In this sense, non-possessive warmth is the atmosphere that promotes and encourages clients to change. The therapist holds positive expectations about the outcome of the helping process and conveys a strong message to the client that the future holds promise of well-being. Freud wrote: "Expectation colored by hope and faith is an effective force with which we have to reckon in all our attempts at treatment." If clients believe that the therapist is competent and helpful, they will respond positively and participate in the helping process.

Full knowledge of another's feelings can be approached but is never fully achieved. Some degree of empathy is needed at the beginning of therapy because, without it, a helping relationship cannot be established. This relationship cannot be artificially constructed by the therapist; it comes into being and grows as therapist and client interact and begin to form a tie of trust based on acceptance and understanding. Clients enter into the relationship in the beginning because they want aid in coping with a difficult situation which they cannot resolve on their own. They do not initially expect to share their feelings openly with the therapist. They usually do not expect that their feelings will be acceptable and have difficulty expressing them openly and honestly. As the relationship develops, clients can overcome this barrier if they believe that the therapist not only understands their feelings, but finds them acceptable.

Genuineness and Congruence. The notion of genuineness is one of the principal dimensions of the helping relationship. Genuineness refers to counselors "being themselves" or being "real." It is best understood as the absence of phoniness or defensiveness on the part of the therapist, but genuineness is not synonymous with total honesty. It does not mean that therapists should reveal themselves completely. Therapists do sometimes have negative responses. If they do, they must refrain from using them in ways that are destructive to their clients.

At the lowest level of genuineness, the therapist is clearly defensive and there is considerable discrepancy between what he says and what he actually feels. In such cases, the therapist may say that he is not at all bothered by the client's anger, but his strained tone of voice contradicts what he says.

In some cases, the therapist is implicitly defensive or excessively professional although there is no explicit evidence that he is not being genuine. At the highest level of congruence, the therapist is fully aware of his reactions and can be open to a variety of feelings, both pleasant and hurtful. Although the counselor has contradictory feelings, they are nevertheless accepted without retreating to a professional facade that covers up or obscures his reactions to the client. At this stage, it is clear that the therapist is being himself, whether he is giving advice, reflecting or interpreting. His verbalizations match his inner experience, and he is free to be himself and, at the same time, can use his genuine responses in a constructive way.

To incorporate genuineness in their relation to clients, counselors and therapists need to be aware of the feelings and attitudes they bring to the helping process. The capacity to be sensitive to one's own internal workings and values and stand back to acknowledge that these inner states play a part in the relationship to the clients. As Compton points out, self-awareness is not easily attained:

> Like all other human beings, social workers cannot make themselves over simply because they wish to do so. Like all other human beings, they are the product of their physical and intellectual attributes, they are shaped by the range, the expansiveness and richness of their life experience . . . and by how they have used these experiences in developing their basic beliefs, attitudes and values (p. 86).

When working with the elderly, it is especially important that the counselor examine his or her attitudes toward aging and recognize that past experiences with older persons (parents, grandparents and other) may color his or her feelings toward an aging client. Otherwise negative reactions that are perhaps hidden and unrecognized may influence the outcome of the helping process.

IV. PSYCHOSOCIAL THERAPY:

A Casework Approach

Psychosocial therapy is a term coined by Florence Hollis to describe a social casework approach to counseling. Central to this approach is the "person-in-his-situation" concept as the basis for helping. Hollis points out that both the person and the social environment are taken into consideration in psychosocial therapy. She writes:

> Focus is always on the person-situation gestalt, which is seen as an interacting balance of forces between the needs of the person and the influence upon him of the environment. Individual functioning is the end result of a complicated interaction between complementary parts of the personality highly susceptible to outside influence. In psychosocial therapy influence is brought to bear on either the environment or the personality or both (p. 34).

The purpose of psychosocial therapy is to help clients cope with external reality more adequately and reduce the press imposed by the social environment. The end result of social casework is an improvement in the social functioning of the client and an ability to handle current life situations realistically.

Supportive Casework

Supportive casework practice has long been recognized as a useful approach in helping people cope with a wide range of situations and can be effective in working with older persons who present emotional problems. This model of intervention is not designed to bring about fundamental changes in the client's personality through the uncovering of internalized conflicts. However, it is appropriate in working with older persons who have suffered loss in ego functioning or who are threatened by an external event. Older persons are likely to experience simultaneous losses: the death of friends, afflictions of the body and mind, loss of social relationships, occupation, role status and possessions. The impact of these accumulated losses produces severe stress and can precipitate emotional breakdown. Moreover, these losses occur in the later years when individuals have less psychic and physical energy to cope with problems. Therefore, a supportive relationship that helps older persons cope with loss is a critical component of the helping process.

Goal of Supportive Casework. Supportive casework is based on the view that aging involves a depletion of resources to cope with loss and regards regression as a non-pathological defense among elderly persons. Older persons are often dependent on others and must rely on them to sustain them when their own physical and emotional resources are insufficient. Regression is therefore seen as a legitimate defense and accepted as a natural outgrowth of the relationship that develops in the course of working with older persons. In short, the worker lends part of his or her ego strengths to the older client when there are manifest breakdowns in instinctual drives or a disturbance in emotional and mental functioning.

The supportive approach draws heavily on the effectiveness of therapeutic relationship in effective intervention, especially in working with older persons. Helen Perlman (1970) refers to relationship as "the most potent and dynamic power for influence" and points out that a relationship that reflects caring and respect is essential regardless of the theoretical model of helping. "The need for these peculiarly human forms of nourishment is intensified at times of vulnerability, helplessness and stress," she writes. "So it may be expected that a person who finds himself resourceless and empty-handed in the face of a problem will need and want connection with someone who combines caring for him with social power and authority to help him" (p. 150).

The supportive relationship is characterized by a combination of concern and acceptance of the client with a capacity to act effectively on the client's behalf. The effectiveness of the supportive approach depends largely on how empathy, warm acceptance and caring are demonstrated by the helping person. During the early phase of intervention, depending on the worker will be seen as appropriate. As treatment progresses, the client gradually gains confidence in his ability to function independently by identifying with the worker, can incorporate constructive ways of solving problems and terminate the helping process.

Supporting Techniques. Among the techniques employed in supportive casework are: reassurance, validation, positive feedback, acceptance, catharsis, education and provision of concrete services.

Reassurance includes expressions that recognize the individual's capacities and show respect for the client's feelings and needs.

Validation gives positive feedback to clients and demonstrates that they have valuable assets and are regarded as competent persons.

Acceptance indicates to clients that they are considered worthy persons regardless of their social status or personal characteristics.

These techniques involve what Hollis describes as "reflective communications in which the worker attempts to sustain the client through expressions of interest, sympathy and understanding, desire to help, confidence in the client and acceptance of him." The effect of these sustaining communications is to reduce anxiety or increase self-confidence.

Catharsis, ventilation of anger, frustration and hopelessness, are important aspects of supportive casework, especially in helping clients cope with the loss of a loved friend or relative. Older persons are especially vulnerable to anxiety and depression in periods of transition; they often feel lonely and confused by traumatic life events. The presence of someone with whom they can share their feelings is extremely important. As Butler (1975) points out, the act of listening is intrinsically therapeutic. "One function of mental health specialists which has direct application to work with older people is cultivation of the act of listening. The so-called garrulousness of old people and their wish to hold on so tenaciously to someone's attention is a social symptom related to their loneliness. Patience, listening and simply spending meaningful time with them are of great therapeutic value" (p. 230).

Education includes imparting information, giving advice or guidance to older clients and their families in considering alternative solutions to a specific problem. Older persons who have undergone loss in cognitive functioning or who are experiencing a high level of anxiety or depression can benefit from this form of support that compensates for such deficiencies. Advice and guidance are used sparingly and are offered only if clients are unable to make decisions on their own behalf and need to turn to a professional person in whom they can trust.

Providing Concrete Service. Helping clients seek out and use needed concrete services such as health care, financial assistance, nutritional services, recreational programs and homemaker services is an important adjunct in supportive casework. The primary objective is to steer clients to existing services that can meet a specific need. Clients are enabled to negotiate steps they must take to obtain the service of a specific agency or social welfare program. If older persons are able to seek out and use these resources on their own, they are encouraged to do so, but in some instances, the worker may take over for clients to ensure that they receive the help to which they are entitled.

Protective Services. Social casework with older persons who need protection has become a matter of increasing concern. A critical factor in the use of protective services centers around the question of what standards are to be applied in determining if protection is needed and serves the best interest of the client. Various factors enter into making such a determination: the ability of the individual to care for himself physically and financially; whether he has the mental capacity to survive without supervision; and whether he will be exploited or neglected if protection is not available.

Associated with these problems are other questions: Who should assume responsibility for offering protection? Who has the right to intervene when a crucial decision must be made and the client has the capacity to do so? Social workers are often involved in these knotty problems. Although exercising authority in behalf of the client can present a dilemma, a supportive approach does involve the worker in protective measures to prevent neglect and serious deterioration of older persons.

Planning Placement. Supportive casework service is indicated when aged persons must make a change in living arrangements because they are not longer able to care for themselves. Separation anxiety is common among the elderly when they are forced to leave familiar surroundings for a new, unknown place and are deprived of a supporting social network. There is a growing recognition that making a major shift from independence and self-reliance to becoming dependent on others is a difficult transition for older persons and for their families. It usually involves strong emotional reactions from family members and evokes feelings of failure and guilt for all who are concerned about the aged family member. Approaching the need for a change in the care of an older person, therefore, requires special sensitivity to the complex psychological factors involved in making a major change. A supportive relation to the client and the family can ease the pain in carrying out a suitable placement plan, helping the client and family members consider alternative plans, and assisting them in choosing a placement that takes into account the client's needs.

Evaluation of Supportive Casework. The principles and techniques of supportive casework have significant implications for working with older persons who present emotional problems.

First, the emphasis this model places on the casework relationship as an essential component of the therapeutic process is especially applicable to work with elderly persons who are extremely sensitive to rejection, have feelings of low self-esteem and a lack self-confidence. A supportive relationship of concern, empathy and positive regard helps clients regain a sense of mastery over their lives and restores their self-confidence.

Edinburg (1985) points out that a supportive approach is especially well-suited to working with older persons and should not be regarded as a "second-rate" form of psychotherapy.

> Working to help individuals maintain their functioning at the highest level, cope with physical and mental losses, handle death of a spouse or prepare for their own death should be viewed as a highly complex form of intervention and considered extremely important in the mental health of the aged (p. 155).

Second, supportive casework calls attention to loss as the underlying factor in the emotional problems of aging and suggests that sustaining and restitution measures are essential in helping older persons cope with depression, anxiety and other affective disorders. Emotional reactions to cognitive or physical deficiencies are seen as serious problems that require attention. Sustaining clients who undergo such losses is therefore regarded as a form of restitution that enables the individual to survive the trauma and regain a feeling of adequacy and self-worth.

Third, the supportive model places importance on adaptation to the aging process as a core concept. In large measure, this view of helping stems from the theory that human development consists of completing tasks that are commensurate with various life stages. An emotional problem is seen as an unsatisfactory resolution of conflicts that need to be addressed. Erikson suggests that the basic issue individuals must confront in late life involves despair on the one hand or integrity on the other hand. The resolution of this dilemma is germane to the purpose of a supportive casework. The goal is to help persons overcome despair and achieve a sense of fulfillment and satisfaction in old age. Each individual is seen as a valued person who has potentials even in late life, and therapy is directed toward helping them achieve integrity, a sense of satisfaction, and feelings of self-worth.

Finally, supportive casework recognizes that an emotional problem must be seen in its social context; that the person and the social environment are reciprocally interrelated. An emotional problem involves the reaction of a specific individual to a specific situation. As psychosocial casework practice suggests, intervention must take both into account. Supportive casework sustains the person who must cope with environment stress and also gives attention to eliminating the source of stress. Sherman (1981) points out that this person-in-situation approach to helping older people has great merit and warns that the role of the mental health worker can "all too easily become that of technical expert and virtuoso with a bag of scientific techniques and procedures, which can lead to inadequate attention to the pervasive social, medical and economic needs of many elderly individuals."

V. PROBLEM SOLVING:

A Task-Centered Approach

Older persons often face a number of serious problem situations. Some problems are related to deterioration of their physical, mental, or emotional state. Other problems have their origin in environmental conditions that produce stress and anxiety. Some elderly persons are involved in trying to resolve problems in their relationship to family members and other persons with whom they have a difficulty.

Although all clients' problems are unique, older persons have common concerns. These concerns tend to cluster around five or six broad categories: (1) problems in interpersonal relationships; (2) dissatisfaction in social relations; (3) difficulty in making decisions; (4) reaction to emotional stress; (5) inadequate financial or social resources.

Problems in Interpersonal Relationships. Conflict between older persons and their adult children can present serious problems that seem to defy solutions. Older persons may expect their adult children to offer more financial or emotional support than they are prepared to offer. Family members may be overly-solicitous or protective of aging parents and prevent them from managing their own lives and making their own decisions. If the struggle between adult children and their aged parents goes unresolved, the relationship will be seriously damaged and cause the parents to undergo severe emotional pain in old age.

Dissatisfaction in Social Relations. Older persons tend to become socially isolated and lonely. The death of a spouse is a very traumatic event, especially in late life. Older persons have a great need for intimacy and companionship, and unless they find some source of social contact and emotional fulfillment, they may easily become despondent and want to end their lives. The environment in which older persons live may increase social isolation. Transportation facilities may be unavailable or too costly for them to visit friends or attend social events. Fear of crime and lack of security may cause many to remain isolated and prevent them from making normal contacts with others. Loss of health and difficulty in moving about can isolate those who are physically deteriorated. Psychological factors are also barriers to social interaction if older persons are reluctant to initiate contacts because they fear their overtures will be rejected.

Difficulty in Making Decisions. Older persons sometimes experience great anxiety when they are called upon to make decisions. They may lack confidence in their ability to arrive at sound judgments even in minor matters. Their anxiety makes it difficult for them to take a course of action. Procrastination aggravates the problem and increases their emotional discomfort. Most older persons who are indecisive have had problems making decisions most of their lives. As they age, the problems in making decisions persist, and these individuals become overly cautious. Some elderly persons let circumstances determine what will happen. Others permit family members or professionals to make decisions for them.

Reaction to Emotional Stress. When an older person's spouse becomes seriously ill or dies, the survivor undergoes a state of mental confusion that interferes with normal functioning. The loss of an important person can trigger a depression and result in suicidal thoughts or acts. If the loss continues to preoccupy the survivor to the exclusion of other matters, a psychiatric evaluation will be helpful in determining whether the client is seriously disturbed and requires special attention for a deep depression that will not respond to counseling.

Inadequate Financial or Social Resources. A disproportionate number of persons aged 65 or older still live below the poverty line. Many older persons fear that they may not leave enough money to pay their rent, buy food and afford the cost of medical care they badly need. If older persons have no sizeable saving—and very few do—they are very vulnerable.

Some will eventually become homeless, try to survive by panhandling, and rapidly deteriorate physically, mentally and emotionally. Even if older persons have some contact with adult children or relatives, there is a limit to what they can provide. In most cases, it is not possible for the elderly to move in with an adult son or daughter, and the security provided by the extended family is missing in contemporary life. The ultimate fear of older persons is that they will be abandoned, become isolated and be helpless in old age.

The Problem-Solving Model

One of the principal aims of counseling is to help clients solve problems and make decisions. The problem-solving process trains clients to discover for themselves how to respond to a problem situation and decide what course of action is most effective in solving it. The process involves a sequence of steps that will help clients develop their own problem-solving skills.

1. **Recognition of a difficulty.** The problem must be identified by the client and become the center of attention. If the client has only a vague notion of what is wrong, the therapist helps him or her describe the problem in specific terms. The client is also asked to describe how the identified problem affects him or her and how he or she attempts to cope with it.

2. **Analysis of the problem.** The therapist explores the facts that surround the client's problem, the conditions that maintain the problem and an examination of the causes that exacerbate the client's discomfort.

3. **Selecting objectives.** At this point, possible ways to solve the problem must be initiated and considered. Alternative solutions must be weighed and decisions considered. The client is asked to suggest ways to achieve a successful outcome. The alternatives are assessed by the client and the therapist to arrive at an acceptable solution.

4. **Selecting a course of action.** At this stage, the counselor and the client discuss a specific course of action that must be undertaken and outline the exact steps each will take in solving the problem.

5. **Implementing the plan.** In this stage, the course of action is put into effect. Action is based on the previous steps having been completed. This is a crucial point in problem-solving because if the actualization of the plan is not achieved, little change is likely to occur.

6. **Evaluating the solution.** The counselor and the client are continuously monitoring the progress to recognize problems in implementing the plan. This procedure tests whether or not the plan is effective in a real-life situation. If the plan does not achieve the desired outcome, therapist and client reconsider the solution and arrive at a plan that is perceived as more effective.

Task-Centered Practice

To guide practitioners to implement the problem-solving process, Ried and Epstein have developed a structured, short-term method of intervention referred to as "task-centered" practice. Epstein defines this approach as "a technology for alleviating specific target problems perceived by clients, that is, particular problems clients recognize, understand, acknowledge, and want to attend to."

Task-centered casework is designed to help clients resolve problems by carrying out specific tasks that will overcome a presented difficulty. This approach to helping proceeds on the premise that a pragmatic, short-term form of intervention is more likely to succeed than long-term treatment. The model is especially well-adapted in working with older persons because they are usually not amenable to extended treatment programs but do benefit from short-term, goal-limited forms of help.

Unlike traditional models of treatment, task-centered casework does not involve a thorough examination of the client's personality but is concerned primarily with the definition of the problems which the client presents and developing tasks that can resolve the problems. The focus is on courses of action that a client can undertake rather than on the psychodynamics of the client's feeling or behavior.

The structure of task-centered casework has special value in working with the elderly because they respond well if they have a clear understanding of what the helping process involves. Clients are made aware of the role they are required to play in solving their problems and actively participate in determining what they expect to achieve in therapy. Defining specific goals or outcomes motivates older persons to engage in the helping process and solve problems. Limited goals and a clear structure are significant factors in the use of the task-centered approach when working with the elderly because they are more easily understood and readily accepted.

The caseworker is required to play a directive role in the task-centered approach. The client is held to perform certain tasks that are set out in the initial phase of intervention. Attention is focused on the target problems that have been defined by clients rather than on the dysfunctional aspects of their personality. It is based on the premise that casework can only be effective if target problems are clearly defined and clients are willing to take action to resolve them.

Emotional discomfort may at first appear to be inappropriate for the use of a task-centered approach. However, a close examination of such emotional states as depression or anxiety may indicate that specific environmental factors play a significant role in creating the emotional distress. In such cases, the client and worker formulate a program of action that will relieve or remove the source of discomfort. Task-centered casework is therefore limited in application to reactive emotional problems. If depression and anxiety are judged to be due to factors other than the social environment and involve medical or psychiatric dysfunctions, task-centered casework is not an appropriate approach to helping.

A general state of emotional disturbance is not regarded as a suitable target for task-centered intervention. For example, a depressed state that is clearly related to a specific event such as the loss of a spouse can often be identified as the target problem. If the problem is regarded as relating to the loss, the client can take a course of action to reduce the stress caused by the specific event. The caseworker engages clients in developing a course of action that will achieve a certain outcome and enlists their cooperation in carrying out specific tasks.

Techniques of Task-Centered Practice

Task-centered casework is rather tightly structured and consists of a sequence of steps that are essential to the successful outcome of therapy. These steps include: (1) identifying the client's target problem; (2) developing tasks that the client is committed to carry out; (3) implementing the tasks; (4) reviewing the client's progress in solving the problem.

Selecting a Target Problem. In the initial interview, the client describes the nature of the problems that present difficulties. Problems must be defined in specific terms rather than vague generalities. After all problems have been clearly stated, clients are asked to establish priorities in order of importance. The problem with which the client wants help is then circumscribed, and the goal of therapy is clearly stated.

Developing Tasks. After the target problem has been selected and defined, tasks are developed. The tasks are to be undertaken in order to bring about a resolution of the client's problem. It is a statement as to what the client will do and how to do it. Time limits may also be set with the expectation that the designated tasks will be completed within a reasonable period. If clients have difficulty deciding on a course of action, the worker help them explore various ways to approach the problem and choose among alternatives.

In helping clients develop appropriate tasks, several questions are kept in mind. **First:** How strong is the client's motivation to work on the problem? Highly motivated clients will develop tasks on their own initiative and carry them out with little or no help from the worker. A difficult task will be carried out if the client is strongly motivated, while those less strongly motivated should not be expected to complete complex and difficult tasks.

Second: Is the task feasible? Clients vary in their ability to complete a given task. The client's intellectual capacity, use of sound judgment, financial resources and social background are taken into account. Developing a task that is outside the range of the client's ability impedes progress toward a solution of the problem.

Third: Is the course of action the client wishes to take desirable? The caseworker may need to evaluate whether a given course of action would be destructive, rather than beneficial. Calling attention to the consequences of a given course may lead clients to review the problem and choose a more constructive and desirable task and result in a beneficial outcome.

Fourth: How much time is needed to carry out the task? Not all tasks may lend themselves to a definite time limit. In most cases, clients are more likely to work at performing a task if some limits are set.

Fifth: Is the client expected to complete more than one or two tasks? Clients have a limited amount of energy and time to devote to the performance of a task. Therefore, tasks need to be carefully selected. The more difficult or complicated ones can be broken down into components or sub-tasks and completed in some orderly sequence that provides a structure for clients to follow.

Implementing Tasks

After tasks have been formulated, the caseworker is responsible for helping clients carry them out. The following procedures are useful in bringing about completion of assigned tasks.

(1) **Establishing incentives and rationale.** Clients must be convinced that the performance of a task will pay off in solving the target problem. If clients are uncertain as to whether the effort required to complete the task is justified, it may be necessary to modify the task or select another one that provides a stronger incentive. Clients may be motivated by considering the consequences of **not** performing the task and letting the problem go unresolved.

(2) **Simulation, rehearsal and guided practice.** Simulation through role playing is often useful in helping clients approach an unfamiliar situation so that they develop confidence and competence in carrying out a task. Under controlled conditions, clients can rehearse the task before they carry it out. In so doing, clients become aware of the behavior that is required. They may be asked to evaluate their performance and discover ways to improve it.

Guided practice differs from simulation in that clients are asked to perform a task with the worker serving as tutor or coach. This form of helping is useful in situations that require communication with other persons in resolving a problem. For example, the worker may suggest that an aged parent meet with adult children to discuss the need for a protective environment. The worker can encourage the client to express concerns, consider alternatives and give opinions in the presence of family members, thereby enhancing the client's ability to communicate.

(3) **Analyzing obstacles.** In some cases, the client may face serious obstacles that stand in the way of performing a task. The obstacle may sometimes be outside the client's control, and in such cases, the task may need to be reconsidered. Dysfunctional beliefs to which clients hold can also interfere with the performance of tasks. In most cases, clients who express certain false beliefs can modify them if they are asked to explain their source and question their validity. If clients once see that certain beliefs are not grounded in reality, they are better able to undertake the course of action that will resolve their problem.

(4) **Reviewing tasks.** The caseworker can effectively use task-review sessions to involve clients in an evaluation of their progress. Reviewing tasks usually takes place at the beginning of each interview, inquiring as to which tasks have been completed and with special attention to those that seem to be difficult to perform. These review sessions give clients an opportunity to talk about difficulties they are encountering and can lead to a reexamination of their motivation, providing incentives or discussing how the task can help resolve a presented problem. The review may result in the formulation of a different task and a new agreement as to what is to be undertaken. Clients may want to continue to work on additional tasks once they have carried out their original contract. In some cases, an open-ended agreement to work with the client on a long-term basis may be offered if it will benefit the client but, in most cases, the client-worker relation is terminated after the tasks originally defined have been completed.

VI. INTEGRATIVE COUNSELING

Integrative counseling is a helping approach that includes cognitive therapy, behavior modification, and task-centered practice. Edmund Sherman, who developed this model, summarizes the essential features of integrative counseling as follows:

> The central focus of this approach is to identify, use and enhance the normal development of personality functioning in the later years of life as the basis for counseling older persons. The underlying theme of the approach is that certain capacities and strengths are normally developed in the course of aging which enable older persons to overcome the demoralization attendant upon the losses and problems of aging. When these capacities have not become operative because of circumstances or events, they should be uncovered, strengthened and developed in the counseling process (p. 27).

The Integrative Continuum

The central purpose of integrative counseling is to restore a sense of competence in older persons. To accomplish this goal, Sherman has developed a continuum that sets forth the inputs needed in helping older clients. These inputs are divided into four major categories: (1) provide maintenance conditions and services; (2) provide support and coping strategies; (3) encourage internal focus of control; (4) evolve alternative forms of self-evaluation.

Providing maintenance is essential in working with older persons who are living on the edge of poverty and need financial or other concrete assistance. The objective in counseling is to reduce stress due to a situational crisis or problem and to remove impediments that interfere with the individual's social functioning. As a result, the client is helped to achieve a level of functioning that reduces dependence on external sources and increases life satisfaction.

The second group of strategies is designed to stabilize self-esteem, sustain morale and improve coping skills. In this phase of counseling, there is a strong emphasis on encouraging the client to achieve emotional stability through his or her own efforts. Reassurance is essential on the part of the counselor who enables clients to realize that they **do** have competence and skills and that they have demonstrated their ability to cope with problems in the past.

In the third stage, there is still a need for support and reassurance to help clients maintain emotional balance. However, the emphasis is placed on enabling clients to develop coping skills and solve problems on their own. The objective is to increase the client's cognitive mastery and develop a sense of internal control that is an essential component of the integrative counseling process.

The fourth stage focuses on exploring clients' self-image and self-evaluations in an attempt to alter the clients' perception of themselves as helpless and incompetent. Various cognitive therapy techniques are used to bring about changes in self-image and improved self-esteem. Some of these techniques are designed to work on problems of anxiety, and some are helpful in dealing with clients who are depressed. One technique that is particularly helpful in dealing with depression and feelings of uselessness and incompetence is the mastery and pleasure therapy approach developed by Beck. "Cognitive restructuring" is a generic term for a number of cognitive techniques and procedures such as cognitive rehearsal, rational imagery, and disputing dysfunctional thoughts that are impediments to functioning in late life.

The continuum of integrative counseling is illustrated in the following chart that identifies the stages described above.

Components of Integrative Counseling

The integrative model identifies four components that make up the counseling process: (1) the self component; (2) the locus-of-control component; (3) the value component; (4) the morale component.

The Self. Integrative counseling encourages clients to maintain high self-esteem despite the changes that accompany aging. Some older clients compare their ideal self with their real self. If there is a wide discrepancy between how they see themselves and what they ideally want to be or become, despair is likely to follow. If they are willing to accept the real self and judge their worth on what they accomplished during their life span, they are likely to achieve a sense of integrity and a high level of life satisfaction.

Life review is an important part of integrative counselling. Reminiscence enables clients to identify with past achievements and positive events that enhance self-esteem and fortify their self-concept. Life review enables older clients to deal with negative distortions of past events that often cause despair. Clients learn to recognize that they should not hold themselves responsible for events over which they had little or no control.

Encouraging Internal Control. Older persons often feel that they have little or no control over their lives and perceive themselves to be powerless and helpless. As they age, they lose important social roles. They also undergo significant physical and mental declines that make serious inroads on their sense of competence and worth. The result is a subjective emotional state that Sherman describes as a loss of internal control. Integrative counseling is designed to assist older persons to regain a sense of internal control over their lives.

Studies show that older persons who retain a sense of control within themselves are likely to remain active and are better able to adapt to old age. Persons who hold to the external locus of control—who believe that outside forces shape events—are likely to be closed, defensive and have difficulty interacting with other persons.

A series of statements can be used to test whether the client has a sense of internal control. Individuals are asked to check those statements that come closest to their own point of view. Several key statements follow:

1. a. In the long run, people get the respect they deserve.
   b. Unfortunately, an individual's worth often passes unrecognized no matter how hard he tries.
2. a. Becoming a success is a matter of hard work; luck has little or nothing to do with it.
   b. Getting a good job depends mostly on being in the right place at the right time.
3. a. Many times I feel I have little influence over the things that happen to me.
   b. It is impossible for me to believe that chance or luck plays an important role in my life.
4. a. What happens to me is my own doing.
   b. Sometimes I feel that I don't have enough control over the direction my life it taking.

The feeling of control or lack of control should be apparent in the client's responses.

Studies also indicate that older persons who have a strong sense of internal control are less vulnerable to the stress of aging and feel more positive about their lives than those who lack a sense of internal control. Moreover, those who have a good sense of internal control are more likely to respond to counseling. They are also more likely to participate in treatment and counseling.

Integrative counseling aims at teaching clients to develop cognitive mastery over their lives and have confidence in their ability to control their environment. Instead of remaining passive, older clients are encouraged to become active participants in the management of their lives and achieve greater satisfaction as they age.

Evolving Alternative Self-Evaluation

Many older persons have difficulty in making the transition to aging because the values they adopted earlier in their lives are primarily instrumental, i.e., their self-worth is based on whether they are carrying out tasks that society regards as necessary and highly valued. The degree to which clients are struggling to clarify their values can be determined by asking them to agree or disagree with the following statements:

1. A person isn't worth much when he or she is no longer able to carry on as a productive member of the community.
2. Unless I feel that I have accomplished or done something that other people value, I feel quite worthless.
3. When you are no longer contributing in such roles as worker or parent, you can't really have value as a person.
4. A person's worth does not depend on how good a citizen, parent or worker he or she is, but simply that he or she is a human being.

Clients are asked to respond to these statements and make an explicit choice about their values. Their responses are used as a basis for exploring and discussing the values that clients hold and how their value system enhances or diminishes their self-esteem.

The integrative approach holds that there is a natural need and inclination in older persons to fill the role of advisor and teacher. If older clients are encouraged to draw upon their past experience and begin to play an important role, they are likely to strengthen their social competencies and achieve greater self-determination and independence.

Client Morale

To measure clients' morale, Sherman has developed a Life Satisfaction Index. The score on this test is used to make judgments about the level of the client's morale and measure progress or regression during the course of counseling. (See Appendix)

Several other tests have been developed by Sherman, including the following:

Subjective United of Disturbance Scale is used to determine the extent to which a given situation causes anxiety. Clients are asked to rate their anxiety level in regard to specific situations such as driving a car. The results indicate how well the client is able to cope with real or imagined life situations. (Appendix)

Beck Depression Inventory provides a rapid assessment of the severity of a depression. It indicates whether clients view themselves as failures and incompetent persons who can accomplish very little on their own. The inventory also identifies the areas in which the client is emotionally uncomfortable and pinpoints target symptoms in the initial phase of counseling.

Cognitive Mastery Assessment Questionnaire is used to measure the degree to which clients feel they are in control of their lives. Clients are requested to respond to three simple and clear statements to determine how they see themselves.

Semantic Differential Test attempts to measure the discrepancy between the client's ideal self and the actual self. When there is a wide difference between the real self and the ideal self, the client has low self-esteem. As the real self and the ideal self merge, the client experiences an increase in morale and life satisfaction.

Evaluation of Integrative Counseling

Sherman's integrative model of counseling is especially useful in working with the elderly because it is based on an understanding of the psychodynamics of aging. Helping older persons develop constructive self-images and enabling them to avoid negative perceptions of themselves is given high priority in this approach.

The integrative model employees a number of techniques that are borrowed from cognitive therapy. To achieve the goal of greater life satisfaction, the counselor seeks to change destructive and distorted perceptions of reality and enable older persons to develop positive ways of thinking about themselves, establish an internal sense of control and achieve a higher level of functioning.

The integrative approach also borrows techniques that are associated with traditional casework, especially supportive techniques that are effective in sustaining the client's competence. Some techniques borrowed from integrative counseling are used in task-centered practices. These techniques help clients develop a capacity to identify problems more clearly and solve them more effectively.

The melding of various approaches in the integrative model of counseling is described by Sherman:

> Fortunately, there has been a coming together of disparate schools of thought in the form of common practice approaches. Thus, as noted, there has been a melding of some cognitive and behavioral approaches and a more general acceptance and incorporation of the core conditions (warmth, empathy and genuineness) in the various schools of counseling and psychotherapy (p. 67).

Sherman points out that the particular techniques the counselor employs may include a wide range of approaches to helping the elderly. He writes: "It is evident that any approach capable of dealing with the immediate and indeterminate problems of living while helping aging individuals in the ultimate resolution of life's last tasks has to be eclective in nature. That is in fact what the integrative approach is all about" (p. 67).

The central theme of integrative counseling is unique in that it is a "psychophilosophy" that seeks to help older persons enjoy life here and now by developing a value orientation that brings about a sense of integrity. Sherman believes that the key to successful aging lies in **acceptance.** "The whole approach," he writes, "is compassionate acceptance of self—past, present and future. The ultimate goal, then, is essentially acceptance—acceptance of life as a process, rather than a possession in a larger scheme of things" (p. 239).

VII. BEHAVIORAL AND COGNITIVE THERAPY

Behavioral therapy and cognitive therapy have emerged as alternatives to traditional models in the treatment of emotional problems. Behavioral therapy is designed to decrease unwanted behavior and increase desired behavior. Cognitive therapy attempts to change thought patterns that are destructive and substitute patterns that improve and facilitate the client's functioning.

Behavioral Approach

The behavioral model avoids the traditional approach of lumping all kinds of "emotional problems" into one category. An emotional problem is always framed in terms of a specific response to a specific situation. Therefore, clients are required to give a detailed description of the event that creates anxiety and are trained to cope with this specific situation in certain specific ways.

The behavioral approach to relieving the client's anxiety is based on the view that exaggerated emotional responses to certain situations are learned and maladaptive patterns of behavior can be changed through retraining. The goal of retraining is to diminish or extinguish the anxiety, and help the individual develop new adaptive responses to events that he might have previously avoided.

Systematic Desensitization. This is used to help older persons cope with situations that provoke anxiety. Clients are trained to overcome specific fears such as fears of being institutionalized, of being alone or fear of being rejected. The training usually begins with relaxation techniques in combination with imagery. The client is asked to focus on the fear response. Then focus on the avoidance behavior. These two approaches are usually combined to bring about the desired result. The ultimate goal is to leave the individual and eventually enter the situation or participate in the event that produces the maladaptive behavior.

The behavioral approach was used by Hussian in working with four geriatric patients who experienced extreme anxiety when imagining that they were riding on an elevator. They had resigned themselves to remaining on their own floor in a long-term care facility and given up participating in outdoor activities.

The approach to extinguishing this maladaptive behavior included the following steps: (1) educating the residents about the nature of their anxiety; (2) asking residents to rehearse ways to cope with the anxiety situations and (3) practicing their new skills in an actual life situation.

The residents were first asked to tell the therapist all the "outlandish things" that would happen if they entered the elevator: being trapped, being burned alive, being caught in the doors, and falling down the elevator shaft. After some discussion of these fears, the residents were asked to repeat aloud positive statements such as "when the door opens, I will go inside and hold onto the rails" or "If the door sticks, I will not panic. I will ring the alarm and wait for help to arrive." The residents were then taught to imagine getting into an elevator while they rehearsed the positive statements. At the end of five training sessions, all accompanied the therapist on a one-story elevator ride. Two months later, all were riding the elevator several times a day and experience no anxiety.

Assertion Training. The purpose of Assertion training is designed to help clients develop social skills such as refusing requests or disagreeing with others. Many older persons are often pushed aside and are treated in a patronizing manner that undermines self-esteem. Although some elderly persons avoid being demeaned or treated with cold indifference, many accept an internalized image that seriously limits their interaction with others. They accept the stereotypes of aging that label them as totally inadequate and behave in a manner that reinforces this image. In dealing with everyday situations, they are unable to refuse unreasonable requests, do not stand up for their rights and are dominated by people who take advantage of them. The objective of assertive training is to teach clients a range of behavior that replaces their habitual responses in social situations that require an appropriate degree of assertion.

Assertive training consists of a combination of techniques such as modeling, behavior rehearsal, homework assignments and positive reinforcement. The techniques most frequently used in assertive training involve modeling behavior that clients can use in distressing situations. Clients are then instructed to practice behaving in an assertive manner until they are able to perform the task in a life-situation. The counselor reinforces the efforts that clients make to become assertive by providing successful experiences in being assertive. Assertive training should not be used if clients undergo adverse effects that cause them to withdraw and discontinue the use of new techniques they have been trained to use.

Modeling Behavior is an important component of assertive training that provides an opportunity to learn and perform behaviors that clients have observed. It is particularly helpful to tell clients in advance that they will be asked to reproduce the behavior they have observed. The modeled behavior should be simple enough for clients to perform. It should also be highly discernible to the observer in order that they can readily perform assertive acts. Modeling behavior is successful in most cases if clients are rewarded for their efforts and their new adaptation responses are recognized by the counselor and other persons in their environment.

There are certain optimal conditions that have been found to be effective in changing behavior through modeling:

1. Use models who are important to the observer and who will attract and maintain the observer's attention (e.g., high-status, prestigious models).
2. Show the model being reinforced for prosocial behavior.
3. Reinforce the observer for imitating the model's behavior.
4. Use clear pretherapy instructions; supplement with relaxation training when possible.
5. Use multiple models.
6. Demonstrate clearly the relationship between the events affecting the model and those affecting the client, in terms both of similarity of problem and of age, sex, and race.
7. Provide preliminary incentives for the observer to attend to, and imitate, the model.
8. Progressively increase the difficulty or the fear-arousing value of the modeled behavior.
9. Have the model describe his progress, and provide verbalized guidance or reinforcement (or both).
10. Use repeated modeling experiences.
11. Use repeated practice for the observer.
12. Provide guidance and encouragement during observer practice.
13. Graduate practice exercises (from less to more difficult).
14. Provide feedback for practice.
15. Provide favorable conditions for practice.

16. Arrange for regular reinforcement of newly acquired behavior to insure that it endures.

17. Arrange for reinforcement from the natural environment as soon as possible.

18. Use guided participation in practicing the real-life behaviors whenever feasible, preferably at each step in the sequence of activities.

19. When using symbolic modeling such as movies, use a combination of audio and visual presentations.

20. Use as many successful exposures—and as much time of exposure—of the observer to the model as possible.

21. Make the modeled behavior clear and highly discernible to the observer.

Modeling is an effective way to decrease anxiety and fear and can be used to supplement a variety of other approaches in behavior modification. When appropriately used, it can be an effective way to develop new behavior, decrease anxiety and fears and increase clients' self-esteem and self-confidence.

Depressive Behavior Problems

Traditional forms of treating depression have given considerable attention to the problem of depression, but the behavioral approach has been rather limited in this regard because it is difficult to identify behavior that reflects depression. The feelings that are associated with depression are highly subjective and difficult to measure in terms that are strictly behavioral.

Despite these difficulties, the behavioral approach can be employed to reactive forms of depression that are caused by certain events such as death of a significant person, loss of job or moving to a new and strange environment. An overwhelming loss brings on feelings of helplessness that often results in depression. The client finds it difficult to replace the lost friend or an important role in the world of work and retreats from active interaction with others and the world around him.

Systematic desensitization has been used in the treatment of prolonged grief reactions after the death of a loved one. The process involves vividly recalling the lost person in very happy situations that occurred in the past. The client is first taught to relax slowly and then call up all the feelings associated with the death itself until the memory ceases to be painful.

Depression may be due to "conditioned helplessness" in which people have been in situations where their efforts to escape have repeatedly failed. They see no hope of a solution to their despair. Clients who have been subjected to stress over a long period of time eventually become exhausted and give up all efforts to change their situation.

Depressed people develop a pattern of not completing tasks because they have not been successful in overcoming stressful situations. To help depressed clients overcome their feeling of helplessness, they are encouraged to finish tasks that are easily within their capacity and involve minimal effort. Clients are encouraged to engage in more difficult tasks and are given positive reinforcement as they gain competence and achieve a sense of self-confidence. The completing of assigned tasks results in a gradual lifting of the depression, and reinforcement by the counselor maintains the client's improved performance and improved emotional state.

Cognitive Therapy Approach

Cognitive therapy attempts to eliminate psychological distress by correcting patterns of thinking that underlie depression, anxiety and other emotional problems. This approach suggests that emotional disorders are derived from distortions and faulty perceptions of reality. Therapy consists of helping clients recognize these distortions, challenging their irrational assumptions, and questioning their interpretation of events. The purpose is to enable clients to give up absurd beliefs and avoid thinking patterns that are the source of their emotional discomfort.

The four basic principles on which cognitive therapy rests are as follows:

First, Mood states depend on what the individual tells himself or herself. If people interpret events as catastrophic, they will be depressed. If they think they will be unable to cope with an event such as illness, they will become helpless.

Second, Imagination and fantasy leave enormous influence over people's emotions. When people are asked to imagine some frightening experience, they react as though it were actually happening. If people are trained to imagine such events without undergoing extreme anxiety, their emotional response will be significantly reduced.

Third, Cognition, emotion and behavior are interrelated. If people change their behavior, they begin to think and feel differently. Moreover, if people think in new ways, they begin to behave differently. Cognitive therapy helps clients recognize the connection between thinking, feeling and behaving.

Fourth, expectations influence behavior. People are influenced by what they expect from themselves and from others. When their expectations are faulty, they are prone to react in a non-rational manner. People may also attribute motives to others that are not true and such false perceptions result in emotional imbalance.

Changing Misconceptions and Faulty Ideas

The cognitive model of counseling is based on the hypothesis that faulty beliefs or convictions can be responsible for emotional problems. Distortions of reality based on irrational misconceptions creates maladaptive ways of coping with difficult life situations and manifestation of symptoms such as excessive anxiety or depression.

The identification of faulty perceptions, beliefs and convictions is the first step in what has been called "cognitive restructuring."

Cognitive restructuring can be achieved by using various techniques, all of them designed to ferret out and change faulty beliefs. Cognitive therapists have developed a systematic approach to cognitive restructuring. The process includes four stages:

1. **Presentation of rationale.** The client is instructed in the way that cognitive restructuring takes place. The explanation is presented in non-technical terms and the client is asked to be willing to proceed and participate in the process.

2. **Overview of irrational assumptions.** A number of irrational self-statements are presented and the client is asked to argue that each statement is rational or irrational.

3. **Analysis of the client's problem.** The client is involved in reviewing specific life situations that present difficulty for him or her. The analysis consists of two phases, (a) the likelihood that the client interpreted the situation correctly; (b) the way in which the client labeled the situation.

4. **Teaching clients to modify internal sentences.** This is what Ellis calls "psychological homework." It consists of a five-step process that modifies clients' anxiety when confronted with situations that they regard as threatening. The client is asked to (a) imagine an anxiety-provoking

situation; (b) the client is asked to evaluate the anxiety he or she is experiencing; (c) he or she is asked to examine how the anxiety elicits self-defeating expectations; (d) the client is then asked to reevaluate these defeating self-statements and perceive them as irrational; (e) clients are asked to evaluate their anxiety level after they have logically considered their irrational self-statements.

The therapist uses this process to help clients recognize that their self-verbalizations—the statements they make to themselves—are the source of their anxiety. After this goal has been accomplished, the therapist helps clients develop constructive, positive verbalizations to take the place of negative self-statements. By identifying the irrational ideas, the therapist illustrates how a faulty perception has led to emotional and behavioral problems and teaches clients that they have control over their emotions once they have changed their accustomed pattern of thinking.

Cognitive Approach to Depression

Studies indicate that the rate of suicide is disproportionately high among the elderly. Depression among the elderly is often due to a negative self-image. They see themselves as inferior and blame themselves for their failures. They also have negative expectations when they undertake a task and anticipate that they will continue to fail in the future. These negative views of the self, the world and the future may result in suicidal wishes.

Aaron Beck has developed a form of cognitive behavior therapy that can be useful in helping depressed clients cope with the problems they encounter. Beck suggests that there are five logical errors that cause people to become depressed: arbitrary inference, selective inference, overgeneralization, magnification and personalization. Beck also suggests that there is a "primary triad in depression." The first component is the pattern of construing experiences in a negative way. Depressed persons interpret trivial events in an exaggerated way, and perceive it to be far more serious than it really is. The second component is a negative view of the self. Clients who are depressed feel that they are inadequate and cannot cope with problems.

Older persons are especially prone to develop negative views about the future. They become apathetic and withdraw from any course of action because they expect it to have a negative outcome. These negative thoughts rob the person of any motivation to do anything constructive about his or her life situation and produce the classical symptoms of depression: sadness, passivity, self-blame, loss of pleasure and suicidal thoughts.

To reinforce changes in thinking, the therapist assigns activities that will provide tangible evidence that the client is capable of completing a course of action. The therapist assigns a simple task that is well within the client's capability. By completing the task, clients begin to change the faulty perception of themselves as inadequate and see themselves as competent rather than inadequate. Homework assignments are given at each session and clients are expected to carry out the assignment. The "success therapy" approach is used to help clients see themselves as more masterful and increase their self-esteem. When other people regard them in a more positive light, clients begin to feel that they are worthy of respect and take pleasure in carrying out assigned tasks.

Challenging Self-Defeating Myths

Older persons are prone to perceive themselves as powerless and inadequate. The cognitive approach can help them overcome these negative perceptions and achieve a higher level of satisfaction and integrity. Among the most common self-defeating misconceptions are the following:

1. **The inevitability myth.** This myth assumes that all older persons are destined to be physically and mentally impaired, and the changes that accompany aging are inevitable and cannot be reversed. Therefore they cannot be successfully treated. The acceptance of this perception causes many older persons to avoid receiving the help of professionals who can sustain and improve their life satisfaction.
2. **Myth of asexuality.** This commonly held belief that older persons have no sexual needs and cannot function as sex partners does a disservice to many elderly persons who want to have a normal and healthy sex life after the age of 60 or 65 and who are capable of enjoying the pleasure of sexual intercourse.
3. **Myth of unproductivity.** This myth is based on the belief that people withdraw from all active pursuits in old age and await the end of life. Older persons who perceive themselves as unproductive

do become withdrawn and may undergo severe states of depression as a result of this self-image. Cognitive therapy can enable older men and women to view their lives in a positive way and enable them to pursue activities that are satisfying and self-enhancing.

VIII. CRISIS INTERVENTION

Crisis intervention is widely used to help people cope with stress. It is especially appropriate in working with older persons who face severe crisis situations: the onset of a life-threatening illness, loss of a loved one, or a drastic change in living arrangements. It is not unusual for these events to follow in rapid succession, increasing the likelihood that accumulated stress will have a devastating effect on older men and women. Unfortunately, these critical life situations come at a time when individuals do not have adequate personal resources to cope with a serious crisis.

Depression often follows a crisis in late life. These depressive states are associated with some form of loss: loss of a family member, change in financial status, loss of an important social role. Deterioration in mental functioning or physical well-being are also common causes for depression in the elderly.

External pressures can cause anxiety states in older persons that escalate into a severe crisis. Many elderly persons live in an environment that is unsafe and fails to provide the security that is so important to their sense of well-being. Lack of financial resources is a problem for many elderly people who have severely limited incomes. Because of chronic illnesses, a disproportionate amount of their income goes toward meeting the high cost of medical care.

The fact that depression, anxiety and other emotional problems among the aged are related to stress indicates that those who work with the elderly must be aware of the need for quick and effective intervention in time of crisis.

Crisis Intervention Model

The stress-related view of emotional disorders suggests that crisis intervention is an effective approach to help older persons cope with anxiety producing situations. The crisis intervention model is a short-term, time-limited form of helping that focuses on the immediate events that bring on depression or anxiety.

The specific goals of crisis intervention can be briefly defined as follows: (1) relief of client's symptoms; (2) restoring the client to the precrisis level of functioning.

Crisis intervention focuses on the present, on the "here and now." The first task is to identify the "hazardous event" that led to the state of crisis and to help clients understand their emotional reaction to the stressful event. The purpose is to help clients grasp the full impact of their situation by describing their experience and analyze how they have attempted to cope with crisis in the past.

Principles of Crisis Intervention. Crisis intervention is based on the theory that individuals are constantly trying to maintain a state of emotional stability. A crisis disrupts this state of equilibrium and produces an emotional problem that overwhelms the person. In attempting to regain a state of emotional balance, individuals go through the following phases:

(1) To resolve a crisis, individuals use the coping mechanisms they have relied on in the past.
(2) An emotional problem results when these responses are not effective in resolving the present problem.
(3) If previous patterns of coping are no longer useful, the individual becomes confused and is unable to solve the problem.
(4) If the individual receives help in understanding the source of the crisis and its effect, the situation can be brought under control and the individual's emotional distress is significantly diminished and the ability to solve problems is restored.

Characteristics of Crisis Intervention. Several factors in crisis intervention distinguish it from other approaches to counseling.

First, crisis intervention focuses on the client's present problem and the events that led to the emotional discomfort. A full psychological evaluation is not useful because a rapid assessment must be made and a course of action must be put into place as soon as possible.

Second, the therapist must quickly engage the client in the helping process. This means that the counselor takes a directive stance at the outset and in some instances may be impelled to give concrete suggestions and advice to bring the crisis under control.

Third, flexibility in the use of various approaches to helping is essential in crisis intervention. The counselor should be able to adapt particular strategies that are needed in a given situation.

Fourth, there must be a minimum delay in offering help, and clients must experience a considerable reduction in their anxiety in the first interview. At the very earliest point, clients must also acquire some promise that they can master tasks that have appeared to be hopeless. Success in short-term therapy depends in large measure on how well clients regain hope that they will be able to master the presented crisis.

Fifth, goals must be clearly defined, and time limits are set to achieve them. The use of time limits tends to significantly increase the client's motivation to work on solving the crisis and prevent tendencies to regress and become overly dependent on the therapist. The acceptance of time limits also has an important bearing on client's self-image and confidence in his/her ability to deal with problems. Clients begin to perceive themselves as competent rather than being "sick."

Sixth, crisis intervention is aimed at helping the client cope with a difficult situation in a rational and constructive way, thereby restoring the sense of confidence that is essential to surviving a traumatic event. The therapist intervenes at a point when the client must summon all his or her resources or be overwhelmed and become helpless in the face of adversity.

Steps in Crisis Intervention

Crisis intervention has no specific structure, but there are identifiable stages or steps that need to be completed in order for the desired outcome to be achieved:

(1) assessing the nature and extent of the crisis;
(2) contracting and setting goals;
(3) outlining the strategy to resolve the crisis.

Assessing the crisis. One of the first tasks is to elucidate and identify the event that precipitated the crisis. Clients sometimes are not aware of the specific source of stress that brought about their depression or anxiety. Even though they can remember the anxiety provoking event, they may not have reported it at the time when it occurred. Consequently, they are unable to connect their disturbed emotional state with any specific time, place or event. In such cases, the therapist helps clients make contact with the specific source of their discomfort.

For example, in the initial interview a depressed client, Mr. T., speaks to the therapist about the reason for his emotional state.

> I'm not sure that anything, anything I know of, had something to do with my being depressed. It seemed to come on me gradually, sort of without warning, but I really felt like a cloud was hanging over me.

As the therapist explored the onset of the client's depression, Mr. T. revealed that he had recently retired from a fifteen-year career as a college professor. He had been a successful teacher, was held in high esteem by his students and his colleagues. For the most part he had enjoyed teaching, but when he reached his 70th birthday, he felt that he should "make room for someone else."

Two or three months after retirement, Mr. T. began to feel unfulfilled and useless. He told the counselor:

> I began to feel that I was not the same person I once was. I had no important work to do—I was bored. Just getting through the day was not easy for me. I guess I felt useless and I felt lost—out of things that mattered.

In this case, Mr. T. was responding to a drastic change in his social role and social status. He was experiencing a personal loss of which he was not fully aware. At some point, he must become aware of how these changes precipitated his depression.

Assessing coping responses. Clients cope with a crisis in various ways, and some older persons tend to regress when confronted with stress and begin to become overly dependent. The regressive behavior is exacerbated because the individual's physical and psychological resources have been depleted. Some older persons react in a totally different way. They claim that they are still able to do everything they once did and refuse to accept the help of others.

Older persons who have a history of a prior affective disorder will usually develop symptoms of depression or severe anxiety. In general, individuals tend to cope with crisis in ways that are most familiar to them and respond in the same way to a new situation. If the established patterns of response does not resolve the problem, most individuals feel helpless in the face of a crisis. The sense of helplessness become self-defeating, lowers self-esteem and undermines the capacity of the individual to cope with the change and loss that accompany aging.

In any case, the initial phase in crisis intervention should accomplish two basic objectives: (1) enable clients to identify the precipitating factor that brought on the crisis and (2) recognize that the defenses and coping mechanisms they use in resolving the crisis are not effective. This initial phase in counseling may be completed in as few as one or two interviews.

Contracting. The second phase of crisis intervention is designed to engage the client in defining the goals that are to be achieved and the time that will be needed to accomplish the goals. The consideration of goals and time limits results in what is sometimes referred to as a contract that spells out mutual expectations and avoids confusion. If clients have a clear understanding of what is involved in the counseling process and make commitments to achieve goals, they are likely to make maximum use of the helping process.

The contracting phase is also designed to restore or enhance the client's sense of autonomy which has been seriously damaged by the crisis. This process starts in the initial interview and continues throughout the course of counseling.

The contract also includes an agreement about time limits. Clients are encouraged to specify how long it will take to solve the problem and determine the frequency of contacts. In most cases, clients choose a series of about six sessions at the start of counseling, but the agreement can be modified in the light of further experience. The use of time limits has two purposes: (1) to push the client toward constructive action and avoid regression, and (2) to maximize the client's capacity for autonomous ability to make decisions.

This phase of crisis intervention is followed by a determination of how the goals are to be achieved. The task of the therapist is explained in terms that the client can understand and recognize as being relevant to resolving the crisis. The specific approach to be employed will depend on the client's needs and the client's ability to work on the problem at hand. The therapist must be able to gain the client's collaboration and be flexible in determining treatment strategy. This requires that the counselor has a wide range of skills and can employ more than one approach in the course of counseling. As Kardever points out: "It is the responsibility of the therapist to fit the therapeutic message with the needs of a given patient, and his particular desired goals, and not the patient's responsibility to fit a uni-model therapist" (p. 8).

Techniques of Crisis Intervention. The use of short-term crisis intervention requires several components that are essential to a successful outcome in counseling.

(1) **Setting time limits.** Some counselors who are accustomed to long-term therapy have difficulty in setting explicit time limits with their clients. Failure to do so may cause the counselor to slip into methods that are appropriate in long-term therapy but defeat the aim of crisis intervention. Attention must be focused on the here and now and issues that relate to how the client is attempting to cope with the immediate crisis.

(2) **Rapid assessment.** Crisis intervention requires the therapist to be skilled at making a rapid assessment of the client's problem within the first or second session. Irrelevant material must be screened out and goals must be formulated as quickly as possible. Expertise in setting goals to be achieved within a specific time frame is an essential quality in crisis intervention.

(3) **Adopting an active role.** Crisis intervention requires the counselor to adopt a directly active role that is in contrast to the more passive stance that characterizes long-term treatment. The clients who face a threatening life situation need to feel that the therapist is playing a major role in the process and has the competence to guide them quickly and effectively toward a resolution of the crisis. At the same time, the therapist must avoid the temptation to become over-controlling.

(4) **Terminating contracts.** The use of time limitations is an integral part of crisis intervention. The counselor must be skilled at terminating intervention and avoid becoming involved in long-term relationships with clients. The goal of crisis intervention is to establish the client's pre-crisis level of functioning and does not include attempts to change basic patterns of behavior or to inquire into all aspects of the presented problem. When the goals of the contract have been achieved, the counselor must be able to separate from the client and terminate therapy.

"Letting go" is not easy for some counselors, especially if the client appears a bit shaky. But it is important to remember that such persons can return for help if they are in need of professional services. Some therapists feel a sense of failure if clients return for more help. As Rapoport points out, it is unrealistic to assume that a problem should be solved for all times.

Reapplication for service should be viewed positively. Experience has shown that clients who return after a brief period of help need even briefer help the second time. They may return because of similar stress; yet the crisis is often less intense. They may use a second period to consolidate previous gains (p. 303).

Moreover, in the process of coping with an existing crisis, clients often develop skills in problem-solving that can be applied to future crisis situations. Termination is based on the belief that clients begin to find solutions and that the objective is to provide them with more adaptive and effective ways of responding to difficult situations.

Application of Crisis Intervention. Crisis intervention is not appropriate for people with marginal levels of functioning or chronic borderline states such as patients discharged from mental hospitals. Candidates for short-term counseling are persons who have a fairly good ego but who are temporarily overwhelmed by a traumatic experience. In some cases, even people with relatively weak ego strengths may be prevented from regressing into more serious disorders through brief intervention.

In all cases, the therapy is aimed at helping clients focus on a rapid mastery of a specific problem and the use of their resources to cope with a crisis situation. This means that crisis intervention strengthens the ego capacities of clients, as Rapoport points out:

> There is a strengthening of coping mechanism and the development of new social and interpersonal skills through imparting knowledge, advice, anticipatory guidance, and rehearsal for reality. There is emphasis on the enlargement of the capacity for prediction and control (p. 301).

For many older persons who are confronted with a crisis that threatens to overwhelm them, crisis intervention is the treatment of choice because it is useful in helping them cope with the problems of aging. It can be an effective approach that not only enables them to deal with an immediate stressful situation, but can also enhance their capacity to deal with problems in the future.

IX. ADJUNCTS TO COUNSELING

There are several areas of counseling that lend themselves to a specialized approach to certain problems of aging. Among these are: family therapy, marriage counseling, sex therapy and retirement counseling. Each approach deals with a specific area that affects other family members—spouse, adult children or others who play an important role in the life of the identified client.

Family Therapy

Family therapy is a relatively new approach to help older persons and their adult children cope with changes in relationship that come with aging. Family members are seen together as a group to discuss the problems that need to be resolved. Through exchange of ideas, aged parents and their adult children find a way to eliminate or reduce conflict that threatens to destroy the family entity.

Identifying Family Problems. Mental health workers have found that one of the problems that needs to be resolved is a reversal in family relationships that occurs as parents age. Adults assume that the parent is no longer capable of functioning as an independent person. They take on a parenting role and arouse resentment on the part of aging parents who reject the notion that they must depend on advice or direction from their children. This situation represents a conflict in perception and feelings between parent and children that can best be resolved if the counselor helps the family identify the problem more clearly and move the members toward a satisfactory answer.

Another common problem in family relationships can be traced to symbiotic ties between an adult child and an aging parent. Parents may have become so involved in the lives of their children that the psychological boundaries between parents and children become blurred. If this symbiotic relationship persists, elderly parents may not be able to let go of their middle age children, or adult children may have difficulty asserting their independence and leading lives separately from their parents. Resolving this pattern of excessive dependence between parents and children becomes more difficult when older parents begin to decline and make increasing demands on their adult children. In some cases, the adult child will engage in what has been described as "fearful withdrawal" in which the children begin to distance themselves from their parents.

The problem of caretaking for older parents may become a major issue for the family. Family members search for an answer to the question: "Who should take charge?" The role of "caretaker" can be a difficult one because the son or daughter who assumes this role can become the object of criticism by brothers or sisters who take little or no responsibility for the care of their parents. Parents sometimes make unreasonable demands and overburden the child who is responsible for their care. The caretaker may take on the role of a martyr and reject other family members' offer to help and share responsibility.

In the course of family therapy, sibling rivalry that can be traced to childhood may emerge. Adult children can still carry over feelings of resentment toward a parent whom they believe preferred a brother or sister and "played favorites" when they were young. Parents may not be aware of how these feelings have affected their relationship to their sons or daughters and are surprised when they are openly expressed in family therapy sessions. They are prone to deny favoritism and discount feelings that disturb other family members. The job of the therapist is to point out how sibling rivalry can be an obstacle to working out the present problem and suggest that the family consider ways in which they can surmount resentment on the part of the adult children toward the aged parent. For the first time, the family may be required to recognize the importance of unexpressed feelings in dealing with one another and find ways of accepting perceptions that are incongruent and move on to a constructive course of action.

Family therapy may also result in expression of guilt and remorse. As parents age, their children may be inclined to regret that they have not been helpful or come to the aid of their father or mother when their assistance was needed. They may be reminded of childhood experiences when they became angry at their parents, were defiant or failed to express affection and respect. The expression of guilt can be therapeutic and bring about closer ties between older parents and their children through reconciliation that heals wounds and creates positive relationships among family members.

Feelings of guilt or anger may remain unexpressed in some families. An adult child may experience anxiety about growing old and enduring the hardships that their parents must endure. The child's anxiety about aging interferes with the solution of family problems, especially if a son or daughter puts distance between him/herself and the aging parent in an effort to avoid disturbing emotions related to sickness and death.

A son or daughter may deny that his/her parents are not physically fit or mentally alert. This denial grows out of their own fear of aging and is an attempt to avoid facing their own demise. As Barbara Silverston points out:

> The feelings we have about our own old age often have a direct bearing on how effectively we can help our parents during their old age and how constructively we plan for our own. People who have a generally positive attitude toward old age—including their own—are more likely to be able to reach out to their elderly parents with concern, compassion and constructive support. If old age appears a time to be dreaded—and many features of modern society suggest that it is—then our own parents' decline may seem very threatening. Their aging seems to toll the bells for our own aging and our inevitable death.

Families also have rules that govern their interaction. Some families have an unspoken rule that feelings should not be openly expressed and that overt display of emotion is not to be tolerated. To abide by this rule, family members must hide behind a facade that prevents them from engaging in an honest and forthright manner. Consequently, the underlying problem is not explored and remains unresolved.

Fear of expressing feelings can be a detriment to progress. The therapist may need to challenge rules that prevent family members from accepting one another's emotional state, such as anger, guilt or disillusionment. To change a long-standing rule can be difficult and is sometimes impossible to achieve. If the family becomes aware that honest exchange of feelings can be useful in understanding the source of their problem, there is a possibility that a new approach will begin to emerge and constructive interpersonal relationships can take place.

The family also defines the roles that each member is expected to carry out. For example, the father may be regarded as the one who makes decisions while the mother plays the role of caretaker. As the father ages, his former capacity to carry out the role of family executive and manager can be impaired, and the family can no longer expect him to carry out the role of decision maker and must look to some other member of the family to carry out this role and accept responsibility for making decisions.

This change can leave the family in a state of confusion. The therapist helps the family recognize how such changes require new definitions of roles and aid them in accommodating to the new situation.

Family relationships can undergo significant change as parents age. One parent may have been dominant during most of the life of the family but is no longer capable of functioning at an optimal level. Such changes may result in reversal of roles. Adult children may begin to play the parental role and parents become dependent on them as their capacity for independence diminishes. In the process of family therapy, the family is helped to determine how the parents' independence can be maintained as they grow old and preserve autonomy for them in later life.

Solving Family Problems. The problem-solving model is useful in family therapy. In the initial phase, the therapist gives a detailed explanation of what is expected from the family and what is to be achieved during the course of therapy. Among the goals to be achieved are the following:

(1) recognizing that there is a problem that family members want to solve
(2) identifying the specific nature of the problem and how it affects family relationships
(3) considering various ways to solve the problem
(4) determining a course of action that family members agree to carry out

In the initial stage of therapy, family members tend to blame some **one** person for creating the problem. These maneuvers are referred to as "scapegoating." Eventually, this scapegoating process proves to be futile and blocks constructive ways to approach the problem. The therapist points out what is happening and helps the family members realize that they cannot continue scapegoating if they are sincere about working out a satisfactory solution. This requires that the family begin to search for solutions that all can accept and embark on a constructive course of action.

The discussion will usually center on one or more specific issues as the family focuses on questions such as the following:

(1) What changes does the family believe need to be made in regard to the relationship between parents and children?

(2) Are these changes feasible? Are they acceptable to the parents? to the children? Can they be achieved?

(3) What specific responsibility must the children assume to carry out the solution?

(4) What changes need to be made on the part of the parents? Are parents willing to make such changes?

The objective in family therapy is to help the family deal with problems in ways that will be least damaging to the parent's well-being and solutions that are acceptable to the adult children. The job of the therapist is to enable family members to communicate in ways that lead to a clearer understanding among all family members. The therapist avoids giving advice, and focuses on helping the family to exercise their own problem-solving skills. In most cases, the outcome is successful if family members join in a constructive exchange of ideas and mutual respect.

Marriage Counseling

Marriage counseling is aimed at helping the partners understand how the changes that come with aging require some modification of their pattern of interaction. Among the changes that have an impact on the marriage are: (1) change in physical functioning; (2) changes in social status; (3) change in roles; (4) changes in sexual functioning.

Changes in physical health can affect the marriage in several important ways. A decline in health creates anxiety in one or both partners. Fear of further decline becomes a concern for the wife who has always depended on her husband to be relatively strong and capable of carrying out certain tasks that he is no longer able to perform. The husband becomes anxious if his wife undergoes a decline in physical energy and finds it difficult to carry out routine household tasks. Perhaps more critical is a decline in the partner's mental functioning that affects all aspects of behavior and can bring about significant changes in personality. Feelings of depression that often accompany psychological and physical decline have a negative impact on the relationship and result in a distancing between the partners.

Changes in social status also have an effect on marital relations. A husband who has had a life-long history of productive work and is forced to retire begins to have problems in adjusting to a change in his status. The wife may be expected to meet all the needs of her husband who makes unreasonable demands on her time and attention. As one wife explained: "John has made me his retirement hobby. He is more than a shadow. He has become my alter ego. He goes wherever I go, and I seldom have a moment to myself. If I go shopping for clothes, he sits there until I am finished. I feel tense and can't shop leisurely as I'd like to do."

When husbands lose their sense of importance, and have no territory of their own, they may begin to encroach on their wife's territory. Some husbands become critical of the way the wife runs the home and tends to be domineering and irritable after they retire. The husband may slip into a state of apathy and depression. Because he has no goal to achieve, he becomes discontent and may begin to blame his wife for his unhappiness. A retired husband explains how his attitude and behavior began to change. His wife confronted him with the affect on their relationship:

> Martha, clearly, directly and withholding no punches, gave me a verbal picture of what I was like now, what I was doing to myself, and what I was doing to her.... The stirring up helped me see how my failure in coping with my reverse in goals was adding to her own problems of adjustment.... I realized then it was up to me to set challenges, goals and purpose for myself that would keep me an alert and active person (Bradford, p. 34).

Marital therapy helps couples set boundaries that define the areas in which each is independent and autonomous. As couples grow older, they often tend to become excessively dependent on each other to fulfill their physical and emotional needs. The tendency toward co-dependence is a natural process and can be mutually helpful. However, the symbiotic ties that develop between husband and wife can place significant limits on their ability to maintain a level of independent functioning that is essential to a satisfying life.

A primary aim of marital counseling is to open up channels of communication between the marriage partners. Each partner has little understanding of what changes have taken place as they grow older. They assume that the partner was the same as in years gone by. Yet they both need to share and communicate about their personal feelings. Therapy enables them to establish ways of accomplishing this mutual sharing experience. Most problems of inadequate communication are the result of a pattern that existed throughout the marriage. To change this familiar pattern requires much effort on the part of both partners.

Open communication is especially important as couples age because they need the support and understanding that is required to cope with the various problems that they confront. Husbands need to appreciate the way their wives feel about aging. Wives need to understand how husbands feel about retirement and the impact of aging on their perceptions of themselves. Unless this mutual sharing takes place, both partners remain separated and lonely.

A problem-solving approach in resolving marital difficulties is usually effective in these situations that are commonly found among elderly couples. This approach is relatively straightforward.

Each partner is asked to define the problem in concrete terms, and the therapist makes certain that both the husband and wife can agree on the "problem-to-be-worked-on." During this initial phase, the therapist avoids exploring the **cause** of the problem in order to prevent the couple from focusing on the "blaming process."

After the couple has clearly identified the problem in concrete terms, they are required to develop alternative solutions. Only one problem is dealt with so that the partners can concentrate and focus their efforts in a constructive way. Each partner can accept or reject a solution offered by the other. This process continues until they agree on a clearly defined solution that they believe will meet their needs and their special situation.

After the couple has arrived at a solution, they agree to carry out the action that is required. In subsequent sessions, they report as to whether the solution actually works. At this point, modifications may be suggested if the proposed solution was "unworkable." After one problem has been resolved, the couple may move on to another difficulty and use the problem-solving approach they have already applied.

The purpose of this procedure is to develop the couple's problem-solving skills while at the same time achieving some success in working on a specific difficulty. In effect, the therapist engages the partners in an exercise in communication in order that they can overcome previous barriers that have frustrated their attempts to deal with marital difficulties.

The outcome of the problem-solving approaches to marriage counseling depends on several factors. Problems of recent origin respond more quickly than those of long standing. Motivation is probably one of the most important factors in determining success. If both partners place a high value on marriage, they will be inclined to make changes needed to keep the relationship viable and satisfactory.

Sex Therapy

Marital partners usually experience some problems in sexual adjustment that are a part of the aging process. Men undergo hormonal
changes and experience a gradual decline in their hormonal level. Most
men have a lower sex drive at about age 50. It takes longer for them to
achieve an erection. However, once the man has become aroused, he can
maintain an erection for a relatively long time. This matches the needs
of most females because they need more time to become fully aroused
and experience orgasm.

The female undergoes a decline in her sexual responsiveness, in part
due to the fact that estrogen and progesterone levels diminish after
menopause. After menopause, the vagina walls become thinner and
vaginal lubrication diminishes. However, the response of the clitoris to
stimulation does not decrease and despite changes in physiology, women
can continue to reach orgasm.

Women are especially sensitive to their appearance, and aging may
cause them to lose their youthful body image. These changes may affect
their attitude toward sex and lower their interest in pursuing an active
sex life. If they feel that they are not sexually attractive, their sex drive is
blunted even though their capacity to engage in sex is not reduced. A
negative image has a negative effect on sexual behavior. If a woman does
not like her body and has a negative perception of herself as a sex
partner, her participation in sexual intercourse may be significantly
reduced and interfere with her capacity to enjoy a healthy sex life.

Marital counseling can address the couples' anxiety about sexual
decline. Studies indicate that those who have been sexually active in
earlier life also remain active in later life. Women who consistently
enjoyed sex throughout their lives engage in sex more frequently than
women who have not enjoyed sex before they reach age 65.

The belief that sexual activity declines rapidly with aging is a miscon-
ception that may seriously affect sexual relations in older couples. They
believe that they should not have sexual desires and a need to be
sexually fulfilled. However, studies by Starr and Weiner indicate that the
average frequency of sexual activity does not rapidly decline. Persons
age 60 to 69 have intercourse 1.5 times per week. Those over age 80 have
an average of intercourse 1.2 times per week. A Consumers Union report
shows that 81 percent of women between age 60 and 70 were sexually
active and 91 percent of the men were sexually active between age 60 and

70. Seventy-nine percent of the men were sexually active at age 70 or older. The Consumer Report also found that 49 percent of women over age 50 reached orgasm almost every time. Moreover, sexual enjoyment did not decline. Of the 800 persons who responded to the survey, 75 percent said that sexual satisfaction was the same or better than when they were younger. The report concludes:

> Far from giving up their sexual drives, those older adults have achieved higher levels of sexual fulfillment. Their comments give power to the belief that the human mind is the most potent sex organ. Sex is better for these respondents because of the greater understanding, increased self-awareness and greater appreciation of the sexual experience—all states of mind that can enhance and even transcend biology.

Assurance that sexual activity is a normal and enjoyable experience for older couples may be effective in many cases where sexual adjustment is a problem. However, there are other cases in which sexual problems are more deep-seated and require the help of a qualified sex therapist.

Most sex therapists follow the procedures developed by Masters and Johnson who pioneered the use of sensate focus exercise to help couples learn to gain a satisfactory approach to sexual pleasure. The application of these techniques in working with older couples is combined with an explanation of how they can bring about significant improvement in the sexual functioning of both the husband and the wife. Masters and Johnson point out that "psychogenic blocking" can prevent older husbands from engaging in sexual intercourse. The difficulty is primarily psychological rather than physical:

> If the aging male does not succeed in talking himself out of effective sexual functioning by worrying about the physiological factors in his sexual response patterns altered by the aging process, if his peers do not destroy his sexual confidence, if he and his partner maintain reasonably good state of health, he certainly can and should continue unencumbered sexual functioning indefinitely.

Only about 10 percent of sexual dysfunctioning is caused by physical factors. The most important impediment to an active sex life among older couples is the negative attitude of society. Older persons are believed to have no need for or interest in sexual gratification. This attitude can prevent many older couples from enjoying sexual pleasure, as Ruth Weg points out:

> Society bestows the meaning and power of sexual expression. The societal endowment of sexuality has been identified with the vitality and desirability

of youth. Middle-aged and older persons can accept, however grudgingly, the inefficiency of the organic system, but the first signs of natural aging in the reproductive system are a threat to identity and an awesome reminder of the rolelessness and sexlessness ahead that society has predicted.

Many sexual problems can be resolved if the partners can communicate and express the need for sexual pleasure to each other and feel free to talk about what pleases and what is a "turn off." As Kaplan points out: "It is extremely helpful to foster a system of open communication between the lovers." Husbands need to know what makes their wives responsive and wives need to tell their mates what is sexually arousing and how they can bring them to orgasm. If the couple is willing to talk about their mutual needs in a non-judgmental way, they can reach a closer, more loving relationship.

Retirement Counseling

Individuals react in various ways to retiring from the workplace. Some welcome retirement and regard it as an opportunity to explore new interests, while others feel that they are forced into a state of uselessness because they have been forced to leave their jobs. For those who have built their lives around achievement and status as the source of their personal identity and self-worth, retirement can be an especially difficult adjustment to make. It is a blow to their self-esteem. They tend to become depressed and go through a period of "goalessness" brought on by an abrupt reversal of roles and goals. In American culture, retirement implies uselessness that leads older persons to perceive themselves as having lost their value and their identity. They may feel that they are powerless and can no longer maintain the status they once held.

In an effort to ward off these negative consequences, some retirees cling to the past. But such reactions rarely help them to make the transition from the world of work. Psychologists point out that a healthy response to retirement can best be achieved by "growth expansion" that helps retirees find new activities that provide a sense of usefulness. This response requires retirees to review their life goals and find alternatives and activities that are conducive to a feeling of satisfaction and worthwhileness.

Most programs that are designed to help older persons adjust to retirement involve a group approach to counseling. The group experience encourages retirees to exchange feelings and share the problems that they are struggling to resolve. The most common issues that emerge in group sessions are loss of the work role, loss of dignity, loss of physical and intellectual capacity. Being able to talk about these losses in the presence of others who are facing the same problems provides a supportive network of understanding and acceptance that leads to the establishment of self-esteem and self confidence. The group process also offers an opportunity for retirees to find solutions that others have discovered and found to be viable and satisfying forms of self-expression.

X. GROUP THERAPY

Group therapy helps older persons cope with a variety of emotional problems that are commonly found among the elderly. The group process also provides the encouragement and empathy that enables group members to solve problems more effectively. Among the benefits that group therapy provides are: a supporting network, breakdown of isolation, opportunity for self-expression, and insight into the nature of their problems.

Providing Support. Older persons often face life situations that create a high level of anxiety and stress. By participating in the group process, members find a sense of belonging that eases the tension and helps them through difficult times. As they see how other group members cope with emotional problems, they begin to gain confidence in their own ability to do the same. Knowing that others have experienced similar problems gives them hope that they also can survive and overcome their difficulties.

The group experience also shows the individuals how they can change their own behavior and pass on information that they have learned. For example, those who have learned to be assertive can model the techniques and behavior to demonstrate how certain behavior can bring about desired changes. Role playing in front of the group reinforces the new behavior and helps members practice what they have observed. Through rehearsal of these new forms of interaction, group members are able to apply them to actual life situations.

Encouraging Self-Expression. Older persons who are reluctant to express their emotions may benefit from the group experience. Some have been severely censored in the past when they revealed anger or were rebuffed when they wanted to express affection and tenderness. The group provides a setting in which individuals can safely reveal that they feel inadequate and incompetent. This may be an uncomfortable experience, but other group members can see many valuable assets that give the discouraged member new confidence. Being considered a valuable member of the group enhances the individual's self image. Moreover, as they

73

begin to help others solve problems, they gain a significant measure of competence and value by contributing to the group process.

Developing Insight. As they observe the behavior of other group members, older persons become aware of the reasons that underlie their own behavior. When they talk about situations that were anxiety provoking, each member can identify with others who have had to cope with such fears. As the events of the past may come into consciousness, each member can speak openly of earlier life experiences that were traumatic.

Achieving Competence. Many older persons have grave concerns about their physical and mental competence and begin to doubt their ability to deal with the day-to-day problems that seem to overwhelm them. The group leader can offer information that is useful to group members who often lack knowledge and information about health services and other sources of community programs that are designed to meet their needs. While education is a part of the group therapist's responsibility, the fundamental purpose is to enable group members to develop problem-solving skills that they can apply to a variety of life situations.

Choosing a Therapeutic Approach. A number of different approaches to group therapy have been developed that are useful in working with the elderly. The behavioral approach can help those who are prone to severe anxiety or who lack assertive behavior skills. Depressed persons can learn to control their thinking processes and overcome their faulty perceptions of themselves and the world around them. Among the specific models of group therapy are: psychotherapy groups, humanistic group therapy, reminiscent therapy and assertion training groups.

Psychotherapy Groups. The purpose of group psychotherapy is to encourage communication among group members and explore the emotional problems that accompany aging. The most common concerns that arise have to do with significant losses: loss in the work role, loss of dignity, loss of family and friends. The group process provides an opportunity for members to talk about these losses and learn that they are not alone. They find a sense of belonging as they participate in group interaction and find that other members will provide support and understanding. Rarely do older persons have such an opportunity to talk about their problems, their feelings and concerns. The group experience helps them to find new ways in coping with the changes that come with growing old and discovering how to make their lives meaningful.

Humanistic Groups. The humanistic group approach is designed to help group members reach what Maslow has called "self-actualization."

Self-actualization includes acceptance of self and acceptance of others and encourages the development of meaningful relationships. This approach focuses on developing strong feelings of self-worth and eliminating anxiety, depression and other emotional problems. Members are enabled to explore their inner selves and begin to grow into a more satisfying relationship to others. Although humanistic group experience does not solve specific problems, it does provide an atmosphere of mutual support and acceptance that can enrich the lives of older persons.

Learning exercises have been developed by Gestalt therapists to enrich the life of group members. These exercises include:

1. Observing other members in the group have meaningful emotional experiences.
2. Self-disclosure and appreciating sharing of feelings with others.
3. Experimenting with new forms of behavior and receiving feedback from group members.
4. Achieving insight into one's own behavior as a result of observation and group interaction.

Such learning exercises must be slow-paced for older persons, but some of them have been used successfully by the Sage Project (Senior Actualization and Growth Experience). Sage improved self-esteem of group members and alleviated depression.

Group Reminiscing Therapy. Reminiscing is characteristically a way in which the elderly adapt to aging. Recalling past events gives group members a sense of continuity and self-identity that might otherwise be lost. Robert Butler points out that the "life review process" can help older persons look at past experiences and integrate them into the here-and-now. Reminiscence also maintains the group members' feeling of pride in their past achievements. Some experiments in the use of group reminiscence have discovered that many older persons who had been sullen and withdrawn at the beginning became active and involved during the course of group therapy.

An experiment with residents of a nursing home indicated that reminiscence therapy can be especially useful in working with depressed persons. Many institutionalized elderly people have begun to lose the feeling of ever having been loved or having accomplished anything in the past. In the group process, they begin to realize that they had many positive life experiences and their self-esteem is significantly increased as a result. Life review also gives older persons a sense of continuity and completeness that might otherwise not be possible.

To make reminiscence therapy achieve a positive outcome, a certain structure needs to be put into place. Some of the guidelines to creating a sound basis for reminiscent therapy include the following:

1. Help members cope with the feelings that are involved when they recall a specific event.
2. Both positive and negative feelings about the event should be expressed.
3. Thoughts and images that come to mind when reminiscing should be connected to the event.
4. Unresolved feeling of guilt or anger toward others in the past should be related to the event.
5. Reactions of other persons involved in the event should be explored.

There are potential dangers in the use of reminiscence therapy. Unpleasant memories may be stirred up and become the source of emotional trauma. The therapist can help the group cope with such problems by comforting the individual or by moving away from the disturbing event. While some members can benefit from a full and free expression of feelings, others need to distance themselves from painful events of the past. The therapist needs to make a careful assessment in each case so that the desired effect can be achieved.

Assertion Training Groups. Many older men and women have developed a pattern of passive behavior that is associated with aging. Assertion training is designed to help them develop assertive behavior through role-playing, modeling and feedback to demonstrate how behavior can be changed. Various exercises are used to reshape group members' thinking and behavior. These exercises are designed to help the group develop a high regard for their own personal rights, discriminate between assertive and aggressive behavior, restructure how they react to specific situations, and rehearse assertive behavior.

The group approach to assertion training is more effective than the individual approach because the group has a greater impact on changing behavior. The group experience is a laboratory where the individual's behavior can be observed by other members. There are other significant advantages to group assertion training.

One, the group helps members see that they are not alone in having difficulty asserting their rights.

Two, individuals can see how other members are making progress in asserting themselves.

Three, the group provides an opportunity for members to practice assertive behavior and learn by doing.

Four, members get feedback from the group and see themselves as others see them. They learn how their behavior affects other people and realize that they need to develop skills in being assertive.

Exercises in assertion training focus on specific situations that call for assertive responses: (a) situations in which someone is doing something that hurts you; (b) making requests of others and denying requests from others; (c) dealing with persons who are overly persistent in making demands. The group members act out each of these situations through role playing and get feedback that reinforces assertive responses. The therapist requests group members to practice assertive behavior in actual life situations and report back to the group.

Reality Orientation Therapy. Older persons who have a history of depression, bipolar disorders or paranoia can benefit from reality orientation. This approach alleviates memory deterioration and confusion by providing mental stimulation and engaging persons in a series of orientation activities on a regular basis. This approach has been used in day care centers and institutions in order to maintain a satisfactory level of functioning. In most cases, certain procedures are employed to keep group members aware of dates and days of the week. A daily schedule is followed. Group members are asked to give answers to questions about the date, time, weather and other information that indicates contact with reality.

Orientation may include instruction in grooming, exercise sessions and small classroom sessions that keep older persons mentally alert. Simple memory games help stimulate recall ability. Although the main purpose of a reality orientation is to reorient confused people, it can also be used to prevent confusion from occurring. In both instances, the reorientation process can help many older persons continue to function with a minimum of assistance. The program is being widely used because it is not difficult to put into place and does not require a highly trained staff to carry it out. Many of the procedures fit into the nursing schedule of nursing and are flexible enough to be implemented in a variety of settings.

Remotivation Therapy. Remotivation is a form of group therapy that stimulates and revitalizes older persons. The goal is achieved through a series of planned meetings with small groups of five to twelve persons who come together to discuss a topic designated by the group leader. The material may include events such as vacations or shopping trips. Each member is asked to gather information for each session and participate in the discussion. Topics that deal with the individual's problems are avoided. Discussion is focused on matters that constitute the real world and thing to which group members can relate. Visual aids and appropriate objects are used to keep the members attention and encourage their reaction.

The first few minutes of each session are devoted to exchanging greetings and establishing friendly relations among group members. Reminiscing is encouraged and members share their experiences, talk about former roles and meaningful events earlier in their lives. The group begins to take on an important role in the life of older persons, provides an opportunity for a healthy interaction with others and helps maintain self-esteem.

Self-Help Groups. Self-supporting groups are usually formed by peers who come together to satisfy a common need or cope with a specific problem. Sometimes referred to as "coping groups," these spontaneous and nonprofessional groups have an important role in providing emotional support and practical help to older persons. Most self-help groups form a network that extends to face-to-face or telephone contacts if members need immediate help and the group is not available.

Self-help groups are formed to meet a wide range of problems including widowhood, retirement, and physical or mental illness. The basic helping activities that these groups provide include: (1) **mutual affirmation**— assuring one another that they are important and worthy persons; (2) **explanation** —a better understanding of one's self and reactions to certain life situations; (3) **empathy** —demonstrating a sincere and genuine interest in the welfare of others. By sharing experiences, thoughts and feelings, group members are assured that their problems can be solved and difficulties can be overcome.

Although group therapy takes several forms, there is a common core of the group process that is useful in working with older clients in a variety of settings. The group experience creates an opportunity for social interaction with others and provides emotional support as members learn how to cope with some of the problems associated with aging. The feeling of belonging to a group may be the only source of identity that some older persons can find to meet their emotional needs. Because older persons are often isolated, group approaches offer a way for them to establish friendships and relationships to others that enhance their lives.

Implementing Group Therapy

Planning group therapy begins with a clear definition of the purpose for which the group is formed. Generally, the formation of a particular group of individuals is based on a common problem that all members are trying to resolve or achieving a specific level of competence in one or more areas of functioning. The purpose of the group provides the basis for selecting individuals who are to be included in the group. Older persons who are experiencing difficulty in adjusting to retirement have a common purpose in joining a group. Older persons who are concerned about marital problems or sexual relations can share common concerns that lead them to join a group of married couples having similar problems. The purpose of the group may be closely related to a specific setting, such as a nursing home or institution that provides term care for severely impaired elderly persons.

Forming a Group. Each potential member is assessed to determine if they can benefit from the group experience. The following questions will help in making a decision as to whether a given individual should be included.

1. Does the individual genuinely wish to make changes in some aspect of his/her life situation, behavior, or relationship to other persons?
2. Does the individual demonstrate the capability of interacting with other persons in the group and using the help of other group members?
3. Is the individual willing to accept feedback from others and consider the opinion of group members in seeking a solution to his/her problems?
4. Is the problem that the individual presents such that it can be dealt with in a group approach and one that others can relate to in a constructive way?

Orienting Group Members. A group goes through several stages before the members feel a sense of "we-ness" that binds them into a cohesive group. Developing trust is one of the essential components of group therapy. Older persons may be uncertain and anxious when they first enter the group. They may be unsure as to whether they will be accepted, can trust other members and confide in them. The therapist can reduce the level of anxiety by creating an atmosphere that promotes trust and leads to a healthy sharing among all group members as they begin to interact with less hesitance and reluctance to discuss their problems. Under the therapist's guidance, the group begins to establish a positive relationship in the first session. The feeling of respect and trust among group members is essential if the experience is to benefit all the members.

It is important to give a clear explanation of the purpose of the group and provide an opportunity for each individual to state his/her own reasons for joining the group. The purpose should relate to some specific objective that the individuals want to achieve and relate their individual goals to the overall purpose of a group. The group therapist also states in clear terms which is expected from the members regarding regular attendance and active participation in group sessions. Some older persons may express concern about whether they can attend if they are ill or have no transportation available to bring them to the group meetings. These matters should be dealt with at the outset to prevent problems that may retard the pursuit of therapy.

Facilitating Group Interaction. At the beginning, most older persons lack the skills in communication that are an essential element in group therapy. The therapist assumes major responsibility to help members develop this skill by modeling and demonstrating effective communication. By restating a message that a group member is trying to express, the group begins to understand how meanings can be clarified by testing out how a message is perceived and if the interpretation accurately expresses the meaning. In some cases, there are blocks to communication due to hostility based on differences in cultural background or basic values. The group may have difficulty dealing with these barriers in the early stages of therapy. The therapist needs to call attention to how such differences hamper communication and openly discuss the feelings involved in relating to persons who are different. If these matters are discussed openly and honestly at the outset, the group can move on to develop a sense of cohesiveness despite difference in background or life situation.

Enhancing Competence. Various group therapy projects are designed to improve the competence of older persons. In some cases, the objective is fairly simple, such as reality orientation for older persons who are experiencing recall difficulties or who are confused about the time and place. In other cases, the objective is more ambiguous. For example, humanistic groups or psychotherapy groups may aim at self-examination and the development of a high level of satisfaction and improved self-esteem. Other groups may be related to a special problem that needs to be resolved such as adjustment to retirement or improvement in marital relations. These latter groups are problem oriented and can benefit from learning problem-solving skills. In each case, the therapist chooses the approach that will increase the group members' competence in a given area. The choice of techniques employed by the therapist also depends on the area which is the target problem. In some cases, the use of role-playing and modeling is a technique that helps older persons cope with anxiety. Rehearsal of new behaviors may be an effective way to help older persons restructure their behavior to achieve a higher level of competence in dealing with difficult life situations. Group members become aware of the changes that are needed to adjust to the problems of aging.

Practical Aspects. Planning a group program for the elderly must take into account several practical matters that make it an experience that older persons can enjoy at the same time that they benefit from the group activity:

1. Transportation may need to be provided for some members who cannot travel on their own but would otherwise attend the sessions.
2. The length of the sessions should take into account the energy level of the participants.
3. The environment must be physically comfortable because older persons can't tolerate extreme cold temperatures, noise and other distractions.
4. Meetings should be held in the daytime hours because many older persons will not leave their homes after dark. Mornings are the best time of day, especially for depressed persons.
5. Physical ailments and hearing loss are often handicaps that need to be taken into consideration so allowances can be made for their limitations.
6. Provide simple refreshments at the beginning of the session to create a ritual that is familiar to everyone.

The group therapist needs to acknowledge each individual member and indicate that everyone is considered a valued individual who can make a significant contribution to the group process.

XI. COPING WITH DYING

Terminal illness is a trying experience for older persons and their families. To help patients and their loved ones cope with the physical and emotional problems involved in dying is one of the most difficult and demanding tasks of those who work with the elderly. Accepting death is at best extremely difficult for most people. Dying is so painful that there is a conspiracy of silence that cuts off honest communication between patient and doctor, between family and patient. Older persons often are unable to share their fear of death and feel lonely and isolated at a time when they badly need the understanding and help of others.

Fear of Death. There are several reasons that make dying and death a frightening experience. Fear of physical suffering is among the most common reasons. During a terminal illness, many older persons have persistent pain, may lose bladder control, have difficult breathing and other distressing symptoms. However, physicians have a wide choice of drugs that can greatly reduce or control pain.

Many older persons fear that they will no longer be able to dress or feed themselves without the help of others. Those who place a high value on independence resent having to take help from others. A terminal illness also has a severe impact on self-image. Those who have been active and vigorous view illness as a severe blow to their egos.

Death also represents a separation from valued persons—a son or daughter, husband or wife. The family begins to view the ill member in a new perspective. The end of a relationship can be a traumatic experience for both parents and children or husband and wife. A dying husband may fear that his wife will not be able to care for herself without his help. A surviving mate fears living alone and losing the affection and companionship that marked their life together.

Emotional Responses to Dying

Kubler-Ross, a psychiatrist who studied the reaction to dying, found that most persons go through five distinct phases: denial, anger, bargaining, depression and acceptance.

Denial and Isolation. When they learn that they are terminally ill, most patients deny that they are dying. They may insist that some mistake has been made and request more laboratory tests or X-rays to prove that the first results were not conclusive. Or they may seek out other physicians to prove that the diagnosis was inaccurate. Some put a more comfortable interpretation on the diagnosis by saying they only need rest because they have been trying to do too much.

Some patients ignore the diagnosis and act as though they are going to survive. They may refuse to accept treatment and do not follow the doctor's orders. In other cases, the patients insist that they have never been told that they are terminally ill.

Anger. When older persons face death, they may begin to complain that they are being neglected by the doctor or nurses even though they are receiving good care. They begin to make angry demands on the nursing staff. Such hostile behavior is often a bid for attention, and most patients gradually begin to become less demanding if they feel that they are respected and valued human beings. Those who care for the terminally ill must be able to exercise patience and realize that they are lightning rods that attract the patient's hostility. Moreover, the expression of anger usually brings some relief to dying persons and is a normal outlet for the emotions that accompany the illness.

Bargaining. Dying persons sometimes use bargaining as a way to face death. It is as if the patient is saying: "I'll be good if you let me live." Bargaining is used to get a "second chance" in the hope that death can be staved off if certain promises are fulfilled.

Depression. Once the inevitability of death is seen as a reality, most patients go through a period of depression. Kubler-Ross refers to this as "precipatory grief" and suggests that silent understanding is more helpful than attempts to cheer patients up: "The patient should not be encouraged to look at the sunny side of things," says Kubler-Ross. It is contraindicated to tell him not to be sad. Family members often attempt to cheer a dying patient and are unprepared to cope with the state of sadness that is a natural part of dying. Family members need to be aware that there is little need for words at this point. A touch of the hand, a stroking of the hair, or just sitting together in silence is the most effective way for families to support the patient during this stage.

Acceptance. After patients have had enough time to mourn, they move on to accepting death with a quiet expectation. Patients do not usually express many strong feelings, and communication usually takes a non-verbal form. As Kubler-Ross suggests, moments of silence may be the most meaningful form of communication:

> The patient may just make a gesture for us to sit down for a while. He may just hold our hand and ask us to sit in silence. . . . We may just let him know that it is alright just to say nothing when the important things are taken care of and it is only a question of time when he can close his eyes forever. It may assure him that he is not left alone when he is no longer talking and a pressure of the hand, a look, a leaning back in the pillow may say more than noisy words.

Helping Patients Cope

If those who care for the dying take a positive approach and are unafraid to talk with patients about their impending death, the patient will be better able to prepare for the end of life, as Cecily Saunders discovered in working with terminally-ill cancer patients:

> To talk of approaching death when it has become inevitable is not mere resignation on the part of the patient nor defeatism or neglect on the part of the doctor. . . . The patient may well achieve more in this part of his life than in any other, making of it a real reconciliation and fulfillment.

Patients want to know the truth because they really can honestly and openly face death in a more constructive way when doctors and family members do not pretend that death is not inevitable. Yet doctors often avoid telling patients that they are terminally ill because they are not comfortable in admitting that medical science cannot always save life. Doctors who are unafraid to face their own death are able to help patients go through the denial phase and tell them the truth.

Dr. Avery Weisman, psychiatrist, has discovered that most patients have a profound sense of relief if they are told that their illness cannot be cured. But if doctors do not help patients work through their feelings about dying, patients become isolated, and most face death on their own. A dying patient describes the pain of isolation:

> I'm just the old helpless case in the corner bed; forgotten. If I cry out no one will hear me. I don't expect to be found. No one will look for me; nobody knows I'm lost. . . . I believe the fear could be eliminated if the

doctor would only talk it over with us. Little by little, we could work with him, to face the end.

Dying with Dignity

To die with dignity is a fundamental right to older persons who are facing a terminal illness. If older persons are to die with dignity, the caretaker's attention must be centered on relieving the patient's discomfort. The pain that often accompanies a terminal illness can be unremitting and needs to be controlled, or better yet, eliminated. Withholding painkilling drugs until the patient demands relief is unnecessary and can lead to acute misery for older persons. Dying patients can be given frequent dosages of analgesics to assure that they need not suffer and reduce the anxiety of having to endure pain.

Equal attention needs to be given to the psychological and emotional aspects of dying. When attention is completely focused on the progress of the disease, the dying patient feels a loss of dignity and perceives that he or she is not valued as a person. Older persons need to be treated with dignity and a sense of caring that is expressed in holding hands, caressing the face, or stroking the hair. These non-verbal communications give the patient a feeling of being loved and valued.

Many dying persons fear that they will be forgotten and deserted at death and will die alone. Doctor Kubler-Ross describes what death means to those who are terminally ill: "We have learned that for the patient, death itself is not the problem, but dying is feared because of the accompanying sense of hopelessness, helplessness and isolation." The dying patient's right to dignity at the end of life is set forth in the following "Dying Patient's Bill of Rights."

The Dying Patient's Bill of Rights

- I have the right to be treated as a living human being until I die.
- I have the right to maintain a sense of hopefulness however changing its focus may be.
- I have the right to be cared for by those who can maintain a sense of hopefulness however changing this might be.
- I have the right to express my feelings and emotions about my approaching death in my own way.
- I have the right to participate in decisions concerning my care.

- I have the right to expect continuing medical and nursing attention even though "cure" goals must be changed to "comfort" goals.
- I have the right not to die alone.
- I have the right to be free from pain.
- I have the right to have my questions answered honestly.
- I have the right not to be deceived.
- I have the right to have help from and for my family in accepting my death.
- I have the right to die in peace and dignity.
- I have the right to retain my individuality and not be judged for my decisions which may be contrary to beliefs of others.
- I have the right to discuss and enlarge my religious and/or spiritual experiences, whatever these may mean to others.
- I have the right to expect that the sanctity of the human body will be respected after death.
- I have the right to be cared for by caring, sensitive, knowledgeable people who will attempt to understand my needs and will be able to gain some satisfaction in helping me face my death.

The Helping Process

Working with dying persons is a very difficult and complicated process, but it can be a constructive and challenging undertaking. In approaching this important responsibility, mental health workers need a clear understanding of the questions that have to be addressed, including the following:

1. What is the goal in working with terminally ill patients and their families?
2. What is the relationship between therapist and patient during this crucial period?
3. What responsibility does the counselor have to the patient's family?
4. How can the counselor be prepared to carry out these tasks?

Goals in Treatment

When patients are inevitably going to die, the goal of treatment is to make the end of life as painless as possible rather than to aggressively attempt to prolong the patient's life. As Avery Weisman points out, the chief obligation of caretakers is to provide "safe conduct for the dying patient." To provide this safe conduct, the medical team and mental health staff must direct their efforts to achieve the following objectives: (1) free the patient from physical pain; (2) help patients cope with the emotional problems associated with dying; (3) assist the family members to accept the loss of a valued person.

Freeing Patients From Pain. Many patients have severe pain that makes the dying process a terrible ordeal and know that they are completely dependent on the doctor to provide relief. Doctors have now recognized that the wise choice is to prevent the occurrence of pain before it becomes unbearable. Cecily Saunders who has had extensive experience in working with the terminally ill points out that pain can be controlled without concern about addiction to narcotics:

> The problems of tolerance and dependence can be almost eliminated by the way in which the administration of drugs is managed. It should be part of the whole process of caring for the patient. . . . If every time the patient has a pain he must ask somebody else for something to relieve it, it reminds him that he is dependent on another person. But if instead, the staff can anticipate the occurrence of pain . . . the patient does not continually ask for relief. He can stay alert, thinking of other things and "forgetting" the pain.

Relieving Emotional Suffering. The emotional suffering that dying patients endure is often more devastating than the physical pain they undergo. The loss of self-esteem and feelings of isolation make dying a traumatic experience, but physicians, social workers, nurses and clergy can do a great deal to diminish emotional and mental anguish. In addition, volunteers are often well-suited to provide the psychological support that patients need.

Family members may find it extremely difficult to cope with the patient's emotional reactions to death. Although there is a need to talk about relationships between the patient, family members are reluctant to communicate their feelings to loved ones. During this period, powerful emotions begin to surface. The family may go through a guilt-ridden phase, blame themselves for failing to provide the care or the affection that the parent needed.

This is also a time for "anticipatory bereavement" that prepares the family for the death of the older person. The task of the counselor is to help the family achieve a state of creative grief as described by Dr. Austin Kutscher:

> The grief experience can be transformed into a most meaningful and productive one through emphasis on the concepts and ideals of creative grief. The energies expended in grieving can be channeled with enormous productivity

into good works or deeds, service to others in distress, or devotion to tasks left undone by the deceased rather than dissipated in unstructured, self-pitying melancholia. (p.21).

Learning to Work with the Dying

Learning to work with the dying requires a period of adjustment to work through feelings about death and become comfortable in relating to those whose life is coming to an end. Bernice Harper has developed a systematic way that counselors, nurses and mental health workers find useful in working with the terminally ill. The process involves five stage: (1) knowledge and anxiety; (2) emotional survival; (3) depression; (4) emotional arrival; (5) deep compassion. These stages are charted in the "Line of Comfort Ability in Figure 1. and extend over a period of 12 to 24 months.

Stage 1. During the initial phase, much of the work involves meeting the patient's tangible requests. The relationship is quite superficial and there is little discussion and exchange about the matters that are the uppermost concerns of the dying patient.

Stage 2. During this phase, the worker becomes aware of the meaning of dying but the main concern is still focused on the disease and the false hope that the patient will survive. At this point, the nursing staff begins to become more emotionally involved with the patient and there is an attempt to deal with fears of death.

Stage 3. At this stage depression is a widespread reaction to the patient's dying and there is a deeper involvement with the patient. This is a crucial stage in the helping process and tests the worker's capacity to overcome frustration and help patients cope with dying.

Stage 4. This stage includes a change in the attitude of workers based on a better understanding of the patient's need to be prepared for death. A close and intimate relationship with the patient is now part of the helping process.

Stage 5. At this point, workers are at the optimum level of helping dying patients. There is an acceptance of death as a natural process and feeling of competence in working with persons at the end of life.

To work with the terminally ill requires the highest level of empathy and understanding. It is also a task that can bring comfort not only to older persons at the end of life, but to their families. This is the challenge and the satisfaction that comes with knowing that older persons need not die alone but are valued even to the very end.

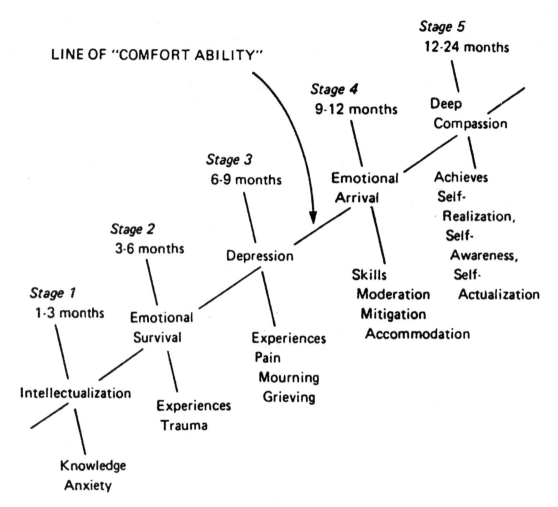

Figure 1. Coping with Professional Anxiety in Terminal Illness. From Bernice Catherine Harper, *Death: The Coping Mechanism of the Health Professional* (Greenville, South Carolina: Southeastern University Press, 1977). Reprinted with permission.)

REFERENCES

Beck, Aaron. *Cognitive Behavior Therapy and the Emotional Disorders.* New York: International U. Press, 1976.

Butler, R.N. The life review: an interpretation of reminiscence in the aged. *Psychiatry, 26:* 65–76, 1963.

Compton, B. *Social Work Process.* Belmont, CA, 1989.

Corey, G. *Group: Process and Practice.* Monterey, CA: Brooks-Cole, 1977.

Cormican, E.J. Task-centered model for work with the aged. *Social Casework, 58:* 490–94, 1977.

Ellis, A. *Handbook of Rational Emotive Therapy.* New York: Springer, 1977.

Edinberg, M.A. *Mental Health Practice with the Elderly.* Englewood Cliff, NJ: Prentice-Hall, 1985.

Hollis, F. Casework: *A Psychosocial Therapy.* New York: Random House, 1972.

Hussian, R.A. *Geriatric Psychology.* New York: Van Nostrand, Reinhold, 1981.

Kardner, S.H. A methodological approach to crisis therapy. *American Journal of Psychotherapy, 29:* 4–13, 1975.

Kubler-Ross, E. *On Death and Dying.* New York: Macmillan, 1969.

Kutner, B. et al. *Five Hundred Over Sixty.* New York: Sage Foundation, 1956.

Masters, W. and V. Johnson. *Human Sexual Inadequacy.* Boston, MA: Little Brown, 1970.

Perlman, H.H. The problem-solving model in social casework. In: Roberts, R. and Nee, R. (Eds.), *Theories of Social Casework.* Chicago: University of Chicago Press, 1970.

Rappoport, L. Crisis intervention as a mode of brief treatment. In Roberts and Nee (Eds.), *Theories of Social Casework.* Chicago: University of Chicago Press, 1970, pp. 267–311.

Reid, W.J., and L. Epstein. *Task-Centered Casework.* New York: Columbia University Press, 1972.

Sherman, E. *Counseling the Aging: an Integrative Approach.* New York: Free Press, 1981.

Weisman, A. *On Dying and Denying.* New York: Behavioral Publ., 1972.

Zarit, S.H. *Aging and Mental Disorders.* New York: Free Press, 1980.

APPENDIX

Figure 1.   Short Mental Status Questionnaire
Figure 2.   Zung Self-Rated Depression Scale
Figure 3.   Beck Depression Inventory
Figure 4.   Philadelphia Geriatric Center Morale Scale
Figure 5.   Life Satisfaction Index
Figure 6.   Assessment Outline

Figure 1. Short Portable Mental Status Questionnaire (SPMSQ)

Short Portable Mental Status Questionnaire (SPMSW)

1. What is the date today (month/day/year)?
2. What day of the week is it?
3. What is the name of this place?
4. What is your telephone number? (If no telephone, what is your street address?)
5. How old are you?
6. When were you born (month/day/year)?
7. Who is the current president of the United States?
8. Who was the president just before him?
9. What was your mother's maiden name?
10. Subtract 3 from 20 and keep subtracting from each new number you get, all the way down.

> 0–2 errors = intact
> 3–4 errors = mild intellectual impairment
> 5–7 errors = moderate intellectual impairment
> 8–10 errors = severe intellectual impairment

Allow one more error if subject had only grade school education.
Allow one fewer error if subject has had education beyond high school.
Allow one more error for blacks, regardless of education criteria.

Source: Duke University. (1978). Center for the Study of Aging and Human Development. Multidimensional functional assessment: The OARS methodology. Durham, N.C.: Duke University.

Figure 2. Examples of Scales to Measure Affective Status

Zung Self-Rated Depression Scale

1. I feel downhearted and blue.[a]
2. Morning is when I feel the best.

3. I have crying spells or feel like it.
4. I have trouble sleeping at night.
5. I can eat as much as I used to.
6. I still enjoy sex.
7. I notice that I am losing weight.
8. I have trouble with constipation.
9. My heart beats faster than usual.
10. I get tired for no reason.
11. My mind is as clear as it used to be.
12. I find it easy to do the things I used to.
13. I am restless and can't keep still.
14. I feel hopeful about the future.
15. I am more irritable than usual.
16. I find it easy to make decisions.
17. I feel that I am useful and needed.
18. My life is pretty full.
19. I feel that others would be better off if I were dead.
20. I still enjoy the things I used to do.

[a]For each item, the respondent rates the statement as "a little of the time," "some of the time," "good part of the time," or "most of the time."

Figure 3. Examples of Scales to Measure Affective Status

Modified Beck Depression Inventory[b]

1. I do not feel sad.
   I feel sad.
   I am sad all the time and can't snap out of it.
   I am so sad or unhappy that I can't stand it.
2. I am not particularly discouraged about the future.
3. I do feel like a failure.
4. I get as much satisfaction out of things as I used to.
5. I don't feel particularly guilty.
6. I don't feel I am being punished.
7. I don't feel disappointed in myself.
8. I don't feel I am any worse than anyone else.
9. I don't have thoughts of killing myself.
10. I don't cry any more than usual.
11. I am no more irritated now than I ever am.
12. I have not lost interest in other people.
13. I make decisions about as well as I ever could.
14. I don't worry that I look worse than I used to.
15. I can work about as well as I used to.
16. I can sleep as well as usual.
17. I don't get any more tired than usual.
18. My appetite is no worse than usual.

19. I haven't lost much weight, if any, lately.
20. I am no more worried about my health than usual.
21. I have not noticed any recent change in my interest in sex.

[b]Each item has 4–5 responses, representing a range of mood; the respondent picks the one most appropriate. We included all four responses only for item no. 1.

Sources: Zung scale adapted from W.W.K. Zung. (1965). A self-rating depression scale. *Archives of General Psychiatry,* 12, 73–70. Beck inventory from A.T. Beck et al. (1961). An inventory for measuring depression. *Archives of General Psychiatry,* 4, 53–63.

Figure 4. Examples of Scales Measuring Subjective Well-Being in the Elderly

Philadelphia Geriatric Center Morale Scale

1. Things keep getting worse as I get older (No)[a]
2. I have as much pep as I did last year. (Yes)
3. How much do you feel lonely? (Not much)
4. Little things bother me more this year. (No)
5. I see enough of my friends and relatives. (Yes)
6. As you get older, you are less useful. (No)
7. If you could live where you wanted, where would you live? (Here)
8. I sometimes worry so much that I can't sleep. (No)
9. As I get older, things are (better, worse, the same) than/as I thought they'd be. (Better)
10. I sometimes feel that life isn't worth living. (No)
11. I am as happy now as I was when I was younger. (Yes)
12. Most days I have plenty to do. (No)
13. I have a lot to be sad about. (No)
14. People had it better in the old days. (No)
15. I am afraid of a lot of things. (No)
16. My health is (good, not so good). (Good)
17. I get mad more than I used to. (No)
18. Life is hard for me most of the time. (No)
19. How satisfied are you with your life today? (Satisfied)
20. I take things hard. (No)
21. A person has to live for today and not worry about tomorrow. (Yes)
22. I get upset easily. (No)

[a]The correct answer, shown in parentheses, is scored one point.

Figure 5. Examples of Scales Measuring Subjective Well-Being in the Elderly

Life Satisfaction Index (LSI–A)

Here are some statements about life in general that people feel differently about. Would you read each statement in the list and, if you agree with it, put a check mark in the space "agree." If you do not agree, put a check mark in the space under "disagree." If you are not sure one way or the other, put a check mark in the space "?."

1. As I grow older, things seem better than I thought they would be. (Agree)
2. I have gotten more of the breaks in life than most of the people I know. (Agree)

3. This is the dreariest time of my life. (Disagree)
4. I am just as happy as when I was younger. (Agree)
5. My life could be happier than it is now. (Disagree)
6. These are the best years of my life. (Agree)
7. Most of the things I do are boring or monotonous. (Disagree)
8. I expect some interesting and pleasant things to happen to me in the future. (Agree)
9. The things I do are as interesting to me as they ever were. (Agree)
10. I feel old and tired. (Disagree)
11. I feel my age, but it doesn't bother me. (Agree)
12. As I look back on my life, I am fairly well satisfied. (Agree)
13. I would not change my past life, even if I could. (Agree)
14. Compared to other people my age, I've made a lot of foolish decisions in my life. (Disagree)
15. Compared to other people my age, I make a good appearance. (Agree)
16. I have made plans for things I'll be doing a month or a year from now. (Agree)
17. When I think back over my life, I didn't get most of the important things I wanted. (Disagree)
18. Compared to other people, I get down in the dumps too often. (Disagree)
19. I've gotten pretty much what I expected out of life. (Agree)
20. In spite of what people say, the lot of the average man is getting worse, not better. (Disagree)

Sources: Moral scale adapted from M.P. Lawton. (1972). The dimensions of morale. In D. Kent R. Kastenbaum, and S. Sherwood (Eds.), *Research planning, and action for the elderly.* New York: Behavioral Publications. Life satisfaction index adapted from R.J. Havinghurst, B.L. Neugarten, and S.S. Tobin. (1961). The measurement of life satisfaction. *Journal of Gerontology,* 16, 134–143.

ASSESSMENT OUTLINE

I. Presented Problems
    A. Physical functioning
        1. acute or chronic disease
        2. systemic malfunctioning
        3. biochemical imbalance
        4. physical impairment
        5. organic brain disease
    B. Cognitive functioning
        1. incoherent or illogical thinking
        2. delusional, obsessive thoughts
        3. deficits in immediate recall or long-term memory
        4. disorientation to time and place
        5. mental confusion
    C. Affective functioning
        1. apathy and indifference
        2. feelings of guilt and self-blame
        3. sense of loneliness and isolation
        4. expressions of helplessness or hopelessness
        5. withdrawal from social contacts
        6. anxiety or agitation
        7. perception of self
    D. Responses to stress
        1. denial
        2. fixation
        3. regression
        4. counterphobia
        5. idealization
        6. ritualistic behavior
II. Social Environment Assessment
    A. Physical characteristics
        1. living arrangements
        2. financial resources
        3. health services
        4. protective services

    B. Social network
        1.   relation to family members
        2.   relation to peers
III. Summary

ASSESSMENT PROTOCOL BOOKLET

Suggested uses: To record identifying data and diagnostic findings.
To present an over-view of counseling process.
To report therapy progress.

Counseling Older Persons: **A Handbook** contains rationale, procedures,
processes, goals of therapy; also includes
diagnostic and treatment methods listed in
Protocol Booklet. Use of this Handbook is
recommended.

I. Identifying Information   Date

Name: Address: Tel. #

Date of Birth: Marital Status:

Family Members   Relation to Client

Remarks:

_____

_____

_____

_____

_____

_____

II. Diagnostic Findings

Physical Functioning

Cognitive Functioning

Affective Functioning

Response to Stress

Social Environment

Social Network

Family Relationships

Summary

III. Therapy Progress Notes

No.	Date	Observations

Termination Status

INDEX

A

Acceptance, 19–22, 25
Affective states, 93–94
Aging, 10–11
    attitudes toward, 20–21
    effects of, 5–8
    problems of, 10–11
    stereotypes of, 9–10
Assertion training, 44, 76–77

B

Behavior modification, 16–17
Behavioral therapy, 43–47
    modeling and, 45

C

Catharsis, 25
Client morale, 40–42
    cognitive mastery and, 40
    measurement of, 41
    self-evaluation and, 40
Cognitive restructuring, 38
Cognitive therapy, 17–18, 47–48
    steps in, 48
Concrete services, 25–26
Congruence, 20–21
Contracting, 57
Coping responses, 56–57
Counselors, 13–15
    characteristics of, 14
    evaluation of, 13
    roles of, 15
Crisis assessment, 55
    aging and, 6
Crisis intervention, 15–17, 53–59

    application of, 59
    characteristics of, 54
    principles of, 54
    steps in, 35
    techniques of, 57

D

Death, 83–89
    fear of, 83
    responses to, 84–85
Decision making, 30
Depression, 41, 46
    cognitive approach to, 49–50
    inventory of, 41
Dying, 83–84
    coping with, 85–86
    emotional suffering and, 88
    isolation and, 86
    rights of patients and, 86–87
    working with patients and, 88–90

E

Emotional stress, 30
Empathy, 19
Enabling process, 12–13
Environment, 27–29
Evaluation, 26–28

F

Family problems, 30, 64–65
Family relations, 64
Family therapy, 61–65
    objectives of, 65
    stages in, 64

G

Geriatric counseling, 5–20
  objectives of, 5–7
Group therapy, 73–81
  benefits of, 73–74
  group interaction and, 80
  implementing, 79
  practical aspects of, 81

H

Humanistic groups, 74–75

I

Integrative counseling, 37–42
  central theme of, 42
  components of, 38
  continuum of, 37–38
  evaluation of, 41–42
  features of, 37
  strategies of, 37
Interpersonal relations, 29

M

Marriage counseling, 65–68
  objectives of, 65
  procedures in, 67
Mental status, 93
Myths, 50–51
  asexuality, 50
  inevitability, 50
  unproductive, 50

N

Non-possessive warmth, 19

P

Planning placement, 26
Problem-solving, 5–6, 29–33
  aging and, 30–33
  steps in, 31

Protective services, 26
Psychosocial therapy, 23–28
Psychophilosophy, 42
Psychotherapy groups, 15, 74

R

Rational emotive therapy, 17
Reality orientation therapy, 77
Reassurance, 25
Reminiscing therapy, 75–76
Remotivation therapy, 77–78
Retirement counseling, 70–71

S

Self-awareness, 21
Self-control, 38–41
  internal, 38–39
  tests of, 39
Self-esteem, 6
Self-help groups, 78–79
Sexual activity, 68–70
  attitudes toward, 69–70
  frequency of, 68
  hormonal changes and, 68
  physical factors and, 69
Sex therapy, 68–71
Stress, 7
Supportive casework, 23–28
  education and, 25
  goals of, 24
  techniques of, 25
Systematic desensitization, 43

T

Task-centered counseling, 17–18, 29–35
Task-centered practice, 32–35
  characteristics of, 32
  problem-solving and, 32
  techniques of, 33

V

Validation, 25